Jim Mason 1

What others are saying about this book:

"This manual is the nuts and bolts of roadway repair. There's nothing like it in print today."
—Terry Lukan, Senior Construction Inspector, City of Issaquah

"A well-written and informative book for people who have to deal with road repair issues."
—Bob Sturgis, Vice President, Lakeside Industries

"A treasure-trove of suggestions, recommendations, tips, and examples for anyone who owns or shares a private driveway, as well as anyone who designs, builds, or maintains roadways. Highly informative and entertaining."
—Jim Brisbine, P.E., AMEC Earth & Environmental

"Straight-forward, witty, and a comprehensive presentation that will prove invaluable to landowners, professionals, and land use attorneys."
—Tom Goeltz, Attorney, Davis Wright Tremaine LLP

"Rod is well qualified to write this book having spent a long career in the field of construction most of which was involving roads, bridges, tunnels, and all the elemental parts of their construction. His efforts are to be commended also because he has condensed a library of engineering information into a book that any of us could read and comprehend."
—Lou Haff, P.E., private consultant
and former King County Roads Division Manager

The Complete Guide to Fixing Roads and Driveways

ROAD REPAIR HANDBOOK

BOOK 1 PROJECT LOGIC SERIES

Roderick D. Johnston

TRANS MOUNTAIN PUBLISHING   VENTURE SCOPE INC. FALL CITY, WASHINGTON

Trans Mountain Publishing
Venture Scope Inc.

Fall City, Washington

Library of Congress Control Number: 2002091115

Rod Johnston, Venture Scope Inc.
P.O. Box 1089, Fall City, Washington 98024-1089

Project Logic is a trademark of Venture Scope Inc.

visit: **transmtn.com**

email: RJOHNSTON@transmtn.com

Johnston, Roderick D.
    The road repair handbook : the complete guide to
fixing roads and driveways / Roderick D. Johnston. —
1st ed.
    p. cm. — (Project logic series ; bk. 1)
    Includes index.
    LCCN 2002091115
    ISBN 0-9719872-0-3

    1. Roads—Maintenance and repair—Handbooks, manuals,
etc.   I. Title.

TE220.J64 2002   625.7'6
                      QBI02-200353

This book is dedicated to my grandmother,

Ann Cloud,

the lady by the sea

who always believed in me.

ACKNOWLEDGEMENTS

This book is a caldron of technical information, hard-earned knowledge, and raw experience. It could only have happened by being around strong engineers, able contractors, and an array of characters stretching from Montana to Alaska who inhabit and attempt to fix their roads with everything from chewing tobacco to seven sack, steel reinforced concrete. Naturally, it would be impossible to list, let alone thank, every individual that has seasoned my perspective on road restoration but to all of them, I am indebted.

I also owe great gratitude to my friends; Jim Brisbine, Carl Cangie, Bill Dempsey, Tom Goeltz, Lou Haff, Terry Lukan, Bob Sturgess, Tina Talbot, web designer Ed Hazen, and Gorham Printing. These engineers, construction professionals, and colleagues took the time to review and comment on my writing, resulting in a much stronger book. Of great assistance and counsel was Mimi Berger. She provided inspiration, professional editing, and literary ideas that now freely dance among the pages. Thanks again, Mimi. We'll meet again on book number two. Last but not least, I want to thank my wife Evie and kids who put up with years of late night typing and weekend work. I also want to remember Evie for her comments, criticism, and laughs. Her patience and presence has helped make me what I am today while contributing greatly to the successful completion of this book.

CONTENTS

LIST OF ILLUSTRATIONS

PREFACE

Think of the American dream. Or, any dream for that matter, anywhere. Wherever your mind takes you, wherever you roam, where there's travel, there's a road. It could be narrow, wide, gravelly or paved. It may be yellow bricked, red bricked, or a dusty and dry path to Grandma's house. You can't escape them because the globe is full of roads. They're a part of who we are and everyday, more and more get added to the world's landscape.

Until now, a reference guide hasn't existed for everyday people who tackle road repair. For most people, road restoration has been a crapshoot. Reliance on others for advice, putting faith in the first person that shows up with a load of gravel, and all the while, dealing with new and uglier road problems year in and year out.

Well, an easy to use, authoritative, and complete book on road repair and process is finally here. It's in your hands and just in time, too. As tax revenues shrink and municipal road funding gets funneled into other transportation needs, little remains for the private landowner who needs help in alleviating headaches related to "that darn road." Unfortunately, you've been on your own—but not for long.

Landowners and professionals alike will benefit from relying on this practical handbook. Answers to many commonly asked questions and chronic road repair issues are addressed in a fashion that's thorough and straightforward. You'll learn what works and what doesn't. Logic diagrams help sort and direct you down trails of rational decision-making while an array of exhibits illuminate your path to understanding. The principles outlined in this book will enable you to take charge of, and drive a road restoration project from beginning to end. You'll be equipped to stay ahead of the issues and orchestrate a plan without falling victim to events that could have otherwise been avoided. And with confidence, you'll be able to converse with consultants, engineers, and neighbors on issues related to restoring your road.

But be forewarned. This is *not* a hands-on, how-to book that teaches proper use of a pickaxe, slinging techniques for lifting sections of culvert, or even blade control when crowning a road. Nor is this book an intended substitute for engineering textbooks and standards although, many engineers and construction professionals will surely benefit by absorbing this book's content. No, it's much more than that. It explains why bad things happen to roads and how to cope with them. If you're interested in fixing your road once and for all, turn the page and start reading. While you're at it, pick a copy of this book up for your neighbor. For a change, let someone else come to you with a plan to repair the road. And then together—permanently fix it.

FOREWORD

Two common basic questions in the area of roadway repair are: What is needed? How do I approach this problem? This book presents a very practical guide with answers to these questions and many more. This guide is easy to read, easy to reference, while clearly explaining to the layman, common problems with common solutions to a multitude of road repair.

Especially notable is the ease of which solutions can be found along with procedures clearly outlined with flow charts and diagrams. There is even a section in working with your neighbors (Chapter 6) that is full of good advice to actually get the job done. This pragmatic approach is one that will appeal to you if you are just "trying to get the job done."

The book covers a full spectrum of diagnosis, possible solutions, and good advice to solve your road problems. The reader can truly appreciate not wading through pages of theory, which are lengthy and not necessary for the layman. This is truly a unique book that will be helpful to anyone wanting to construct or repair a roadway. It will also make an excellent reference for civil engineers and contractors. I will certainly have multiple copies available for engineers in our firm.

Concept Engineering, Inc.
Carl Cangie, P.E.

INTRODUCTION

Who Is This Book for?

This book is for people who are serious about fixing private roads and driveways. You might be a homesteader, rural resident, or urban dweller. Perhaps you're an engineer, a contractor, or work for a public municipality. It doesn't matter. If you've memorized every pothole between your kitchen door and the nearest highway, this book is for you.

You already know how to drive in a serpentine manner to avoid puddles, cracked pavement, and unidentified objects sticking out of the surface of your road. You think you have it all figured out until you take a moment to wave at oncoming traffic, or reach for the defroster, or adjust the radio. Then it happens. Bam! You feel betrayed. After all, you thought that you had the lay of this road all figured out.

First, you feel the weight of your car violently jar to one side as your front wheel bangs down hard into what seems like oblivion. Then, as though rising from a storm, your car bellows and rebounds to the maximum limit of flex left in your shock absorbers. That familiar thud reminds you of what you already fear. Your shock absorbers are tired and in need of replacement. Again. You wonder for a moment if more damage is being done to your car than just another routine thrashing to your tired shocks. While contemplating the money and time you will need someday to replace all four shocks, the faint but twangy sound of a recoiling spring catches your attention. It's a new sound that you've never heard before, and you don't like it. For a moment you wonder if car damage sometimes just goes away. Can a car heal itself without need of service or repairs?

This book was written for you; the person who either lives off of a private roadway or who relies on a driveway or unimproved road to cross your property. It was written for those who want to better understand how to plan and manage the time, money, and labor needed for community road repair and improvement. As a tool, this book will serve those who seek direction while navigating their way through a successful road construction project.

I also wrote the book for myself. Having lived and worked on many private and unimproved roadways, I've never had a resource available that I could reference when explaining to a neighbor or client why their roadway cries for them to alter their driving habits. More than once, I could have used a text that clearly explains why it is best not to drive into roadside ditches or how driving habits relate to the formation of potholes. Where could I find a manual that explains in layman's terms why someone's driveway fails every year in spite of the expensive rock that gets plowed into it?

More specifically, why do roadways fall apart? And when they do, how can they be properly restored and maintained by everyday people who do not have deep pockets or an infinite stream of public revenue to draw from?

Civil engineering and obscure construction textbooks missed the mark. Soil, agriculture, and country living journals fail to tackle road restoration issues. The more I looked, the more I realized that nothing of substance existed on the subject of roadway repairs and maintenance.

Hence, this book. Use it as a common denominator when weighing varying opinions within your road association or when dealing with your contractor. Use it as an instructional handbook, a beacon, a guide to helping you achieve better roads and safer access. For the sake of your roadway, your motor vehicle, and your health, please read on.

CHAPTER 1

Living Together on Private Roads

Country road, take me home to my sweet rustic oasis. It's the place where it all happens. It's where we live, play, and raise our families. Nothing is sweeter than returning to our homes and property. And as sweet as it is, landowners experience few things more bitter than watching an extension of their homes and property deteriorate from abuse, over use, and lack of control. As unpalatable as this scenario sounds, it is happening thousands, maybe hundreds of thousands of times a day across America. This book delves into the saga of repairing and restoring dirt, gravel, and hard-surfaced private roads.

Private Roads and Driveways Differ from Public Roads

Private roads and driveways are different from public roads in many ways. Mainly, one is built, restored, and maintained with public funds or taxes and the other isn't. Unfortunately, many of us who buy that special place in the country fail to realize the implications of year-round living on a private road. The rules change when you leave the protection and carefree maintenance of our nation's public roads, and the rules are rapidly changing everyday!

Here are some key differences between private and public roadways:

➤ The private road is all yours. (And sometimes, your neighbors!)

Public agencies manage and maintain our public roadways. When someone trashes a public road, they have trashed public property. Penalties and legal consequences have been established to control and punish those who abuse public property. However, when someone trashes your private road, your options for recourse are limited. In a literal sense, if you can catch them, you get to be judge, jury, and enforcer. Plus, you get to pay out-of-pocket for repairs and maintenance.

With private roadways, you are literally and wholly on your own. When a private road needs snow plowing or a section of the roadway is in danger of washing away due to excessive rainfall, it doesn't automatically receive the attention or services of public works crews. Of course, if an emergency or life-threatening situation develops, a public works agency *might* be counted on to provide support depending on how far out you live and the extent of concurrent attention required within its own public service area. Public crew assistance is, however, the exception and not the rule.

When damages such as cracked pavement, fallen trees, and slope failures occur on private roads, landowners must make a decision. Ignore the problem or fix it. Then, pay for it.

Bankers and titleholders usually require private roadway owners to maintain their roadways. But what does that mean? Maintain your roads to what standard? Who's standard? What should the road look like? What indicates road neglect? In most cases, there exists no standard or identifiable condition to be maintained. At best, acceptable roadway conditions are subjective in nature.

Even so, titleholders rarely venture out to inspect and verify that favorable road conditions are being maintained. The lender's role may further diminish if you or your neighbors own your property outright or if each landowner's title varies with differing requirements and conflicting obligations for access and maintenance. What a mess!

The hard reality is this: if you access your property off a private road, the roadway belongs to both you and your neighbors. Therefore, it is incumbent upon private landowners to maintain and improve their roads as they know best and, unfortunately, at their own expense.

➤ Public and private road standards.

Rest assured that the public roadways you travel—if newly built, enlarged, or recently repaired—have been constructed to an accepted standard. Construction roadway standards vary among municipalities but are usually based on prudent engineering, proven subgrade and pavement design, and competent construction methodology for that region.

Historically, many roads have been constructed to absolutely *no standard*. People built what they had to build in order to travel. Traffic safety was of little concern. When expected to support the weight, speed, and frequency of modern vehicles, these older roads fail. A road suitable for yesterday's mode of transportation can easily result in today's traffic related calamity. So, in order to ensure a baseline for quality, public standards for road construction have been developed. Some examples of public road standards include the following items:

- Minimum roadway width.
- Roadway storm drainage systems.
- Maximum roadway pitch or grade.
- Bike and hiking lanes or sidewalks.
- Degree of required pavement striping.
- Street lighting, signalization, and signage.
- Bridge requirements and culvert protection.
- Minimum thickness of paving and rock subbase.
- Ability of your local fire department to access your land in case of an emergency. (This standard should be considered in any road design whether public or not!)

It is wrong to assume that private roads have been built to the same construction standard as surrounding public roads. If public agency approval is required to construct a private road, municipal inspectors work to ensure that acceptable standards of construction are being followed. They check for permit compliance and make certain that the road is being constructed per plan.

In some cases, real estate developers, landowners, and contractors are not bound to permits or enforceable standards. They can build whatever they want. Wherever they want. They decide how much to invest in quality, longevity, and safety. Some choose to spend whatever money it takes to build a sturdy and safe roadway. Others choose differently. They find it more appealing to invest in low quality and unaesthetic roads. Clean black asphalt and freshly laid gravel look great but it takes time, traffic, and weather to reveal a road's true character.

Progressive developers and those who construct to public standards may establish protective covenants assuring that all future road construction within their development conform to the same set of imposed standards. And that's not all bad. If your goal is to attract public agency interest in your private road, considerations like deeding significant land to right-of-way, installing sidewalks, moving fences, and upgrading private driveway transitions (at your expense) should be factored into your decision-making and budget.

Building to "spec" leaves the door open to having your local government later consider maintaining and owning your roadway. It is easier to persuade a public agency to assume and maintain a private road if the road is built to that agency's standards.

If you are able to build a *new* road without construction permits and would prefer to avoid local public agency standards altogether, you can create your own standards. Alternative, private standards can be developed to ensure whatever level of quality you desire. New private construction standards can reference local municipal standards already on the books, or for reasons of budget and practicality, you can modify them as you see fit.

If you are seeking to have a public agency assume ownership and maintenance of your *existing* private road, it may have to be reconstructed or relocated in order to meet that agency's standards. The magnitude of such reconstruction can be enormous and may end up costing more than new construction of the same roadway!

In situations where no private roadway standards exist, but the local public agency is attempting to enforce an array of constraints on your restoration work, you may be able to negotiate alternative standards or conditions with your permit agency. Negotiating which standards can or should be compromised is a tricky endeavor. After years of constructing roads all over the Pacific Northwest, I am convinced that many opportunities exist where standards and respective costs can be lowered without penalizing construction quality. I also know that there is little room to change standards involving roadway safety. Rule number one: safety is untouchable. Rule number two: seek the advice of a construction consultant or civil engineer who knows sitework if you plan to "tweak" your municipal road construction standards.

Completely revising local municipal standards or radically challenging them as part of a new permit process can be arduous and expensive. Although not commonly recommended, if wholesale changes in standards can be demonstrated to save money without sacrificing quality and safety, it may be well worth the effort. In following this course of action, you risk experiencing any number of difficulties including increased permit process time, possible degraded relations with public agency people, and the likelihood of experiencing difficulty later when trying to persuade the same agency to take ownership and assume maintenance of a road not built to their standards.

Real estate developments contingent on connecting to substandard roads are generally permitted under the condition that existing roadway deficiencies be rectified to a level set by the permitting agency. Depending on the developer's agreement, costs for such improvements may be borne by the developer, the municipality or a combination of both.

Private roadway construction affords flexibility. Flexibility to make spontaneous decisions and quick deals for cheap or suddenly available materials that result in cheaper construction. Conversely, public agencies are not as nimble nor are they as sensitive to minor fluctuations in cost.

One last item worth mentioning. Municipal standards are measured criteria. They comprise a body of work that defines how to construct something suitable within that municipality or jurisdiction. When standards are selected and added to permit documents or become part of an approval process, they are commonly called *specifications*. This is because somebody specified, or selected from a body of standards, conditions for granting your construction permit.

➤ Nonengineered private roads and obsolete alignments.

In many instances, private roadways follow an historic route linked to an ancient footpath or animal trail. Also known as *primitive roads*, these older routes generally exist along land contours that follow the terrain where minimal earthmoving, and easy travel would be encountered.

Some road locations just happened, typically with no record of who built what. Perhaps a farmer or ancient railroad company cut the initial grade and people naturally adopted its logical alignment as suitable for that era's traffic, whether it be a cattle drive or the straightest route to the Saturday night square dance. The problem is that whatever worked for farmer Jack's wagon will probably not work for Jane's Mustang.

Older roadways tend to wind with multiple and varying grades within short distances. If we consider a private road that's loaded with curves, chances are great that a public roadway constructed over the same terrain today would end up straighter with milder grades and safer sight distances.

➤ Private landowners pay at least three times.

Public road restoration and maintenance is financed with tax dollars. Presumably, everyone in your jurisdiction pays taxes; therefore, some form of equity payment is made by all citizens who, in turn, have a right to enjoy public roads.

Conversely, private roadway maintenance expense is an additional cost to the land taxes that you already pay. Private land owners can pay at least three times for roads. Here's how:

1. They pay taxes to build and maintain public roads.

2. They pay out-of-pocket for private road construction expenses.

3. They pay auto repair expenses resulting from unmaintained private road conditions.

The good news is that car damage resulting from shoddy roadways can easily be eliminated and private roadways can be permanently fixed without breaking the bank.

➤ Neighbors and private road associations.

When you purchase rural land that does not front a public roadway, you are purchasing a form of trust. You are trusting that you will always have safe and reliable vehicular access to your property. You are trusting that the road will always be there. It's taken for granted. It's a natural trust based on a series of assumptions that involve people who share the same private road with you.

Your trust, your basic assumptions about your neighbors, should read something like this:

• Your neighbors will want the same road standard and surface treatment as you do.

• Your neighbors will be open and free when communicating about roadway issues.

• Your neighbors have the financial means or work ethic needed to maintain the road.

• Your neighbors will view the roadway as an investment in their own property's value.

• Your neighbors will care about the condition of their

vehicles, driving speed, and safety.

- You can count on your neighbors to show up with a shovel, chainsaw, or checkbook, depending on what immediate roadway issue needs attention.

- You will agree with your neighbors on the obvious and most effective ways to deal with road repairs and maintenance.

- Your neighbors wouldn't attempt doing anything beyond their immediate skills. Like you, they would pursue professional advice if necessary.

As you may already painfully know, one strike in the above eight assumptions can be enough to quench the spirit behind any meaningful roadway repair or maintenance issue. Prepare for the worst. That is, understand that reaching a consensus or getting even close to full agreement amongst neighbors might not ever happen. You cannot be neighbors with those who do not want to be neighbors. You cannot reach those who don't want to be reached, and you certainly cannot teach adults to take care of things that they've never cared about before. Even though it's for their own good, they may resent you for trying. People have differing values, priorities, and wealth. Those all play into the challenge.

So, how do private landowners pull together and make restoration and maintenance happen in an orderly and democratic fashion? They either join an existing association or form a new one consisting of landowners who have vested interests in owning frontage and access onto your private roadway. Small groups usually form amongst friends and neighbors who have similar issues with the road.

The initial group may tackle a minor but sorely needed maintenance task resulting in an immediate improvement to the road. This action can work to demonstrate a sense of purpose and solidarity. It says, *"Look here! This is nothing. We can do more with your help."*

Slowly, others join the group as it expands into a cohesive unit. It may take years. Some neighbors move out while others move in. You may never get full participation but whatever you end up with, the best effort your group can give surely beats doing it yourself. It's certainly worth your time and effort.

Associations or committees meet regularly to discuss needs, finances, and strategy. There develops a sense of agreement. Votes can be taken on new issues and selected individuals may fill positions such as treasurer, secretary, and president.

Good things happen when neighbors come together and talk. More people visit during the year, kids seem to get along better, and, in general, people are happier with where they live. Taken the other direction, I have also witnessed situations where neighbors become so disjointed or in such conflict with each other that progress never occurs toward organizing anything. The key to making road associations function as designed lies in remembering some simple neighborly principles involving honesty, fairness, and friendship. Another necessary element is the need for landowners to recognize the basic fact that everybody has an interest in the road.

One word of caution though. Although there is a place for compromise, there also exists conditions under which doing it only one way will work. That one way is the right way. Know when to be firm, understand the facts, and know when you should yield.

Privately Owned and Maintained Roadways Exist Everywhere

Dirt and gravel roads (also known as *unimproved roads*) serve billions of people around the globe. They provide the way home to our families and investments.

In North America, trends in explosive rural growth combined with a growing lack of public funds have resulted in requiring land developers to construct many of our newer, high-quality, paved roadways. Some jurisdictions aren't allowing development to occur, even on smaller parcels, and when they are allowed to proceed, rural landowners and developers are being required to construct roads to meet public standards.

Regardless of trends in new construction, thousands of miles of private roads already exist and they lay where older roads have been established for years. Most roads predate the landowners who live off of them, leaving nobody with an accurate history of how and why the road was constructed. This presents a number of issues such as:

- Why was the road constructed?
- What occupied the land prior to the roadway?
- Did the roadway evolve from some other land use?
- What type of materials were used in the construction of the road's subgrade?

To Cope or Not to Cope with Roadway Restoration

A recent report issued by the Surface Transportation Policy Project and the Environmental Working Group states that drivers spend roughly $6 billion dollars annually to fix damage to their vehicles due to poor roadway conditions. And, that's just on *public roads*.

There is no estimate for vehicles suffering damages on private roads, yet private roads are usually in worse condition than public roads! Public or private, the amount of money spent repairing vehicles because of poor roadways is more than we ought to spend.

As private roads deteriorate, landowners must cope with repairs as they see fit. This means restoring their road within budget and to the extent that they understand road repairs. Their other choice is to ignore road deterioration and hope it goes away. Of course this doesn't happen. Unrepaired roads grow worse as each season blends into the next while the years continue to roll past.

Poor road conditions can result in any or all of the following:

➤ Car damage.

- Tire damage.
- Filthy vehicles.
- Premature damage to car lights, seats, and rims.
- Windshield and paint finish damaged by flying rock.
- Body rust proliferates when mud holds moisture against unprotected metal.
- Damage to vehicle suspensions, overuse of the clutch and brakes, and alignment problems.

➤ Expenses and bodily stress.

- Reduced gas mileage.
- An uncomfortable ride.
- Proliferation of mystery rattles.
- Bodily injuries can be aggravated and jarring pain may result.
- Depreciated land and home values and unaesthetic neighborhood appeal because of the rugged road conditions.
- "People problems" when neighbors resist new development and growth because additional traffic will accentuate existing roadway problems or when neighbors point fingers at those whose driving habits damage the roadway.
- The promise of a worse road the following year.

➤ Driver safety issues.

- Lack of emergency vehicle access.
- Statistically, more people are killed on rural roads than on urban expressways.

- Vehicle safety hazards develop with uneven road surfaces, lack of medians, hidden ditch lines, and varying grades.

- Seasonal road hazards such as ice develop when moisture pockets freeze. During dry weather, dust and loose soil particles billow when parched roadway sections are disturbed.

Who needs the above? Realizing that the potholes have to go is the first step toward fixing your road. If you are fortunate enough to enjoy a contractor, roadway specialist, or civil engineer as a willing neighbor, count yourself blessed. His or her input and skills will be valuable and you'll be well ahead in the process toward rebuilding your roadway.

If you do not have such resources at your disposal, this book will address many of the questions and concerns that will confront you on the road to restoration.

Remember, if you do not care about your road's appearance and condition, visitors won't care. In this world, people receive a level of caring equal to or worse than the level of caring those same people openly exhibit.

When you allow your roadway to fall apart or you sit idle as others degrade it, you're telling the world that it is okay to abuse your road. Delivery truck drivers won't respect your ditches. Hot rodders won't respect speed signs. Contractors will think nothing of tearing up the road surface by walking a piece of tracked equipment down your asphalt. People won't question whether or not driving off the shoulder is appropriate and these same people won't worry about being "caught" doing so. Oh yeah, let's not forget the beer and soda cans.

✓ More "Do's"

- Slow your vehicle's speed.

- Make safety your first priority.

- Envision what you'd like your road to look like.

- Understand where your public and private roads begin and end.

- Evaluate the link between bodily pain and rough road conditions.

- Talk with your neighbors and casually mention your road's condition.

- Calculate how much money you can personally afford for road restoration.

- Calculate how much money you spend on unimproved road related car damage.

- Visit your library or historical society and research the origins of your private road.

CHAPTER 2

Roadway Decay
and Cheap Improvements

Read Your Land and Determine Its Natural Characteristics

The land on either side of your roadway tells a great deal about your road. When studied, native roadside characteristics and soil can provide you with enough information to get you started on a plan of action. Here are some tips to help interpret your road's natural condition and deficiencies:

1. Native vegetation.

You can get an idea of your subgrade soil type(s) by observing the species and condition of vegetation growing along your roadway. They reveal the extent of your road's soil type, stability, and moisture content.

The presence of water-loving trees such as willows and cottonwoods indicates abundant ground moisture. Broken tops and uprooted stumps can indicate both wet soils and gusty wind patterns. Lack of trees can indicate that the soil provides minimal drainage and, perhaps, rocky and harsh conditions. Leaning trees or groups of trees that exhibit similar bending and curvature within the trunk may indicate moving soils or unstable slopes. Lush green grasses point to abundant moisture and organic soils.

Within your locale, research the types of trees that thrive in dry or well-drained soil conditions. Do they make their home alongside your roadway? If so, your road may not have a subsurface water problem and your soils may be suitable for construction. The same reasoning applies to grasses, forbs, and shrubs. Wetlands tell another tale that involves lots of water and creatures. Wetlands are not conducive to good road building, cheap construction, or saving money.

2. Soils.

Grab some soil in your hand and squeeze it. Does it crumble apart or stick together? If it sticks together and feels mildly moist, your roadway is probably comprised of silts and clays. If the soil crumbles and pours out of your hand, your roadway likely contains sand or coarser materials.

Sandy soils that drain moisture provide far less exposure to water damage than do clays or silty soils. Silts and clay, unless sealed and shaped to shed water, will absorb and hold moisture. Once wet, such soils become unstable. They're prone to swelling and heaving below roadway-running surfaces.

When these soils dry, they shrink, resulting in cracks that lead to potholes and, again, an uneven roadway. Either way, you lose. Clays and silts are bad news for roads unless they are treated and surfaced properly.

Topsoil is another enemy of roadways. It's a haven for moisture and contains organic matter that not only acts like a sponge but, over time, it deteriorates and rots. When topsoil shrinks, your road depresses and becomes susceptible to breaking up. Unless it's used for growing plants or grass along the road's shoulder, there is no place for topsoil in any road section. Topsoil is poison for roadway subgrades.

If you have a cut slope above or below your roadway, during dry weather look for a sheen along a line of strata where the soils change or appear to be different. A sheen indicates seasonal moisture and is a symptom of water. Likewise, strata revealing gravel and rock can also indicate periodic passage of water. During wet weather, seams of coarse material are capable of passing water under your roadway and depositing it down and out of the open cut. Watch for this.

Soil is generally rated by its strength. That is, its ability to resist weight and force. There are many ways to label and determine soil strength but most professionals measure it in terms of the soil's relative compaction (given in percent) or density. Generally, a better compacted or denser soil is able to withstand greater stress before deforming or failing.

By using these simple evaluations, you'll be able to predict with some certainty your road's soil conditions. You can also check local soil surveys or confer with your jurisdiction's road engineering department in order to learn more about your soils. Getting the opinion of a geotechnical soils engineer is always a sure-fire means to understanding your soil situation. Don't hesitate to hire a geotech when in doubt.

3. Water.

Do you see ponds or water collecting adjacent to your roadway? Do open areas adjacent to your roadway contain wetlands or dark soils? Do the remains of older oil slicks line the vegetation along the toe of fill? If so, measure the water levels relative to your road subgrade. Do these water features immediately respond to rainfall or do they gain water over a longer period of time? Depending on the high watermark elevation, the road prism may be holding significant levels of water, thus weakening its structural foundation. Water lubricates soil particles and moving soil erodes roads. Water must be corralled and expelled immediately.

4. Rock.

Exposed bedrock can indicate the presence of continuous rock within your subgrade. This can be good and this can be bad. The good news is that your road may be more stable than you realize.

The bad news comes in two doses. The first involves water. Water migrates downward through the soil until it finds bedrock. Depending upon depth, trouble can occur when it migrates along rock supporting a roadway. Similar to electricity, water constantly seeks a path or direction.

Continuous bedrock sheds and channels water wherever gravity will take it. If the rock forms dips or cavities, it holds water.

The second dose of bad news involves the expense in dealing with hard rock. Modifications to your road alignment and grade involving rock excavation or blasting can cost a great deal of money. Other complications including noise, safety, and replacement material can result in higher construction costs and schedule disruption. Any dealings with rock should include a geologist's or geotechnical engineer's opinion.

Rock that is naturally erosive, porous, or "rotten" will break down when exposed to weather. If you can afford to leave such rock exposed, time will help weaken it and make it somewhat easier to excavate later. The problem with this approach includes dealing with an unfinished cut for an extended period of time while keeping your contractor happy enough to return later in order to finish the job.

The presence of large rocks or boulders creates headaches of a different variety. Ridding your project of boulders can entail such budget busters as rock splitting, bulk excavation, and blasting. In some cases, you may need larger and more specialized equipment. If you yank them out whole, you still have to deal with them in some creative way or pay to have them loaded and hauled off.

Water seeks crevices between large rocks and soil. It migrates into the subgrade and works to weaken it. During cold conditions, frost heave may occur if this water freezes and consequently lifts surrounding rocks higher and through the road's surface.

5. Impact of existing land uses.

What's happening where you live? Is growth occurring along your roadway? Varying adjacent land uses impact your road by increasing traffic volumes, bringing updated construction standards to your neck-of-the-woods and changing the course of storm drainage.

Storm water drainage relates to how land and topography absorb and send excess storm water onto or along your roadway. Adjoining land with paved impervious surfaces, roofs, and compacted earth will shed more water than if the land had been left in its native state. Whether it originates from a point source or sheet flows, storm water must drain and exit somewhere. Is that somewhere onto your roadway?

Do adjoining properties connect to pipes in your roadway? Are there plans to upgrade your road's above ground or underground utilities? What utility systems exist there now? Do they carry fluids, power, gas, or communication lines? Do any of the pipes carrying fluids leak? If so, leaking fluids may be feeding that monster pothole that you can't seem to repair.

Search for roof drain stubs, drainage culverts under driveways, and the ends of storm pipes. It is safe to assume that these pipes are operational and that they pass water even though you may not see any. The presence of thick vegetation at the pipe end could mean water. Follow drainage routes that lead to and leave from your road. Where is water coming from and where is it going? Check these same locations during a significant rain event. Is water backing up or ponding? If so, clean or trim the ditches of vegetation and check to see if any culverts need cleaning. If your work results in altering water flow, be sure to get the water back and flowing clean into its natural channel.

As land use changes, so do the requirements imposed on storm pipe and ditches. While investigating, you may discover that you need more culvert capacity. New culverts should be designed to ensure that they will do the job. They must be able to handle the maximum volume of water draining to them and then some. In some cases, this stands for being able to handle the maximum flows deliverable by inflowing pipes and ditches. Plan for the future. If the road will handle it, install at least the minimum sized pipe as designed and even go a size bigger, especially if you are paving. You don't want to install an under sized pipe, come back and dig it out, replace it, plus cut and repair your pavement. But, beware. You also don't want to adversely affect any downstream property as a result of upsizing a culvert. The increased water flow could cause flooding at the next restriction down gradient. Seek the advice of a contractor or civil engineer to help assist in determining correct culvert size.

Another problem includes run off from clogged drainfields and over used or failing septic systems. Begin by looking for the presence of shallow water and lush growth over an area that is otherwise dry with less surrounding vegetation. Also check public land records for the existence of septic drainfields. You can do this by researching building records and construction permits, health department records, or by talking directly with the landowners themselves. Sometimes you can literally smell trouble. Follow up and determine its source. Where is that stuff going?

Keep in touch with your local public jurisdiction for zoning and planning issues. What is planned for your neighborhood? Investigate large adjacent landowners and developers. Let them know that you exist and that you care about any plans they may be considering in developing property or upgrading the roadway. If you are fortunate enough to meet with project owners who are early in the design and planning process, take advantage by getting involved. Most developers want proactive neighbors. They want as many reasons as possible to gain local approval. You can be part of that effort and get your concerns and issues handled at the same time.

Why Unimproved Dirt and Gravel Roads are Inherently Weak

Unimproved dirt and gravel roads develop potholes, slope failures, and "wrinkles" for a number of reasons. In addition to the natural conditions as explained above, most reasons point to shoddy construction while others suggest too much traffic. The wheels of fast-moving and heavy vehicles act like heat-seeking missiles. They will find and punish all wet and weak areas in roadway surfaces.

Let's explore the primary reasons why unimproved roads fall apart:

➤ Poor original road location.

• Aspect.

Roads facing north and east receive fewer hours of sunlight. This keeps them wet, frozen, and shaded longer than roads on the southern and western sides of slopes, hills, and mountains. These moist conditions create subgrades that are softer for longer periods of time.

- **Steep grades, sharp curves, and inferior roadway alignments.**

Many older existing roads were built for seasonal use. They were intended for lower and slower traffic volumes. Road grades weren't really an issue when the straightest way to market was considered the best way to town. What did matter was the amount of excavation and earthmoving that had to happen in order to build the road. Roads therefore were built to follow topography rather than cutting and filling through it.

As subdivisions and rural development advanced, farms and forested areas were transformed into small acreage parcels and home sites. Farmers and landowners interested in selling or breaking up their property typically punched in roads and utilities with little regard to construction standards. In some cases, the wrong equipment was used in road construction as people used the equipment they had or what they could afford. This resulted in

Figure 2-1. A prime candidate for improvements.

limiting road builders to what they could accomplish. Ultimately, the degree of refinement suffered.

Some public agencies have used existing roads as lines of demarcation when defining how certain parcels and land tracts should be broken up. As a result, many roads, regardless of their grades and alignments, evolved into main access ways. They define today's road system. Many landowners live with steep grades and sharp curves in part because of this.

The point is, most older roads were not built for modern vehicle traffic. The faster we drive on these curves and grades, the more we have to brake, resulting in surface failures and wrinkles.

Accelerating vehicles reaching for grip on steeper slopes cause the subgrade to surrender deeper wet material resulting in potholes and cavitation. Sharp curves shift vehicle weight to the outer wheels causing them to find any weakness in the subgrade. The road develops further surface degradation and chronic failure points atop an already substandard road base.

The unimproved road in Figure 2-1 portrays multiple deficiencies. It's too narrow, too steep, lacks sight distance, and has it's round-rock surfacing thrown to one side. It exhibits rising rock, washboarding, vegetative intrusion, and scouring.

Unimproved roadways tend to fail at the following locations:

1. Within running lanes.
2. Anywhere moisture is present.
3. At transition points where road surface material changes.
4. At narrow road sections where traffic "necks-down" into a concentrated zone.
5. At braking and acceleration zones found on steep road grades or where fast moving traffic halts to a stop.
6. At pivot points such as driveway entrances and intersections or where weight suddenly shifts to the outer wheels such as on sharp curves.

7. At high-impact zones including low areas and dips.
   Unimproved roadways just can't take the extraordinary
   inertia and force resulting from vehicles routinely bottoming out.

8. Under ice. Ice works as an insulator. It keeps subgrades
   soft below it. Wheels spin out of control exerting force
   and vibrations through the ice and into the subgrade
   beneath. This action kneads the subgrade while acting to
   draw water up to the road's surface and under the ice.
   When the ice thaws and breaks up, surface moisture enters
   an already saturated and weakened subgrade. Roads then
   develop potholes and asphalt roadways crack resulting in
   depressions that do not heal. Varying patches of iced and
   clear roadway surfaces cause roads to degrade unevenly.

➤ Poor construction.

• Organics and stumps.

Stumps and organic material from the forest or farmland might never
have been removed from the roadbed. Organic material draws and holds
subsurface moisture and acts as a "cushion," refusing to set up or compact.
As organic material decomposes, it collapses when subject to roadway
duress resulting in cavities or potholes. Once an area collapses into a pothole, it forms a basin that collects yet more surface water runoff and
moisture. As the sides of the pothole soften and fail under loading and
tire shock, the hole grows.

Stumps also cause subgrade failure by sticking up and acting as a hard
platform around which surrounding soil displaces over time. Water finds
the sides of stumps and follows it down into the heart of the road's foundation. The result is accelerated void formation along the sides of the
stump, differential settling, and bone-jarring travel.

Tree species matters in determining the amount of time it will take
for a road to fail. Cedar and redwood stumps degrade slowly, remaining

as part of the roadbed for many years. Pine and hardwoods quickly rot and produce potholes soon thereafter.

• Unsuitable fill dirt and other additives.

Unsuitable fill dirt may be comprised of organic or inorganic soils. Inorganic soils will not work as suitable fill if they are too wet when dumped or placed as road fill. Moisture-ridden soils dumped and remaining in the road base will cause weak spots and lack of compaction thereof, only exacerbates settling. Organic material is unsuitable because it rots, holds water, and won't compact. Mixing organic soils with inorganic soils rarely works since small amounts of organic soil may contaminate and weaken even the best inorganic soils, regardless of how they are placed.

Ditto for wood. Wood has no place in road fills. Some roads have been built using treated wood or have been supported with cross timbers and logs commonly referred to as "corduroy." Granted, these elements can last for years, as ancient Roman excavations prove, but the cost and headaches of installing utilities or excavating through it later aren't worth it. And, don't forget, the Romans didn't drive motor vehicles.

• Poorly drained original soils.

Poorly drained and moisture-sensitive fill material leads to dips and potholes. There is no way around it. If a roadway is built over wetland and swamp terrain without use of adequate fill, fabric, or drainage relief, the road will develop surface failures when exposed to moisture and traffic.

Mechanical kneading from vehicles draws water up towards the roads surface. Vibrations and relentless pounding from traffic works wet subgrades causing them to shift and move. When mixed with seasonal surface water, roads weaken. Mild saturation breeds potholes and mass saturation leads to wholesale failure.

As failure zones develop up and down a road, heavier loads from trucks and higher impact from faster cars continue to find weak spots.

Nothing heals, it only gets worse. Soon, chronic points of surface failure become a permanent fixture on the way to town.

• Lack of roadway subgrade drainage.

As we've explored, water simply destroys roads. Where creeks, ditches, and adjoining lands drain along and across roadways, proper water conveyance systems must be constructed. The energy and volume of running water must be contained and channeled as early as possible. Otherwise, water will have its way, tearing channels and rivulets into the roadway and causing erosion. The results are washed-out roads, exposed rocks, and deeply cut swaths across your road.

Water that is allowed to build up and pond adjacent to roadway subgrades can migrate laterally, saturate the dirt subgrade, and soften it. This leads to potholes and surface failures. In short, roads need to "breathe." They need to be free of water migration and sit higher than the adjacent ground. As a rule, get rid of water as fast as you can.

• Lack of roadway surface drainage.

Unimproved dirt roadways must be graded in order to shed surface run off. Running water will erode and chew away road surfaces in any direction that it's allowed to flow. If a roadway is constructed without adequate surface grading and ditches to carry away and contain water, the roadway will degrade during times of increased moisture and rain. It is always good practice to direct water off of a road's surface and away from tires and foot traffic.

• The wrong rock at the wrong time.

People who do not understand dirt road construction are prone to buy lots of rock. When roads fail and someone cries "more rock," people blindly order rock without knowing what to order and they often do it without seeking qualified advice. In doing so, they leave themselves open to getting rock from some trucker who buys whatever is cheap and handy, or they get whatever rock some pit operator has an overabundance of in his yard. This isn't the way to go.

Once the rock arrives, the usual treatment involves placing it over a bare dirt road surface. If the rock is too small or round, it's not suitable to be placed over bare dirt. If the rock is larger and crushed, it may work but only after the subgrade has been prepared for rock surfacing. We'll discuss these items later in this chapter.

• Lack of compaction.

Compacting dirt during road construction accomplishes three objectives in ensuring roadway life and performance.

1. First, it causes side slopes, layers of fill, and running surface to shed water while reducing the relative area of dirt surfacing. Reduced surface area means that there is less area available to collect and hold moisture.

2. Second, compaction forces dirt to consolidate into a solid and coherent product needed for providing roadway structural support. A by-product of compaction is that it helps to rid soil of air pockets. Air pockets hold water and are susceptible to collapsing under vehicle loading.

3. Third, compaction shapes the road's surface to prepare it for surfacing and traffic.

• Paving over what appears to be a suitable roadbed.

Property on private roadways that attracts today's homeowners also attracts individuals who are serious about caring for their new roadway. These individuals work hard for what they have and they want more. They want healthy lawns, nice gardens, and better roads. They find the money and they find the time to improve and protect their investments. They aren't afraid to roll up their shirtsleeves and grab a shovel.

Many of these people come from city environments. People moving from urban areas to the country. They want and appreciate hard surfacing for what it offers. They may seek it to protect their cars and for cosmetic reasons. Some envision sports courts and roller blades for their kids. For unimproved roadways, this means hard surfacing over an existing subgrade.

Placing hard surfacing over a properly prepared subgrade is fine. The problem lies in placing hard surfaces over a roadbed that is not able or ready to support it (see Figure 2-2). Although an unimproved road may appear stable, it may be soft with weak areas. If these areas are not detected and repaired before paving, the road will not adequately support traffic regardless of your final surfacing.

In addition, if a roadway does not have sufficient rock or free draining material under paving, moisture and water may undermine the surface layer resulting in failure points and sharp-edged potholes. There goes the dream, the money, and your patience.

Figure 2-2. Alligatoring and potholes above failed subgrade.

A secondary concern involves using a contractor that lays less asphalt or concrete than is required for adequate support. Thin spots can prematurely fail leading to further repairs. The mechanics of dealing with hard surfaces is covered in Chapter 4.

➤ Increased traffic volume.

Everyday more people move to the country to enjoy the rural life. More people means increased traffic and increased traffic beats up roadways. With people comes construction, and construction brings contractors and pickups (with nails), dump trucks, logging trucks, lumber and concrete deliveries, fuel trucks, and garbage trucks. When the crowd hits, you'd think that Ford had an assembly plant at the back end of your road. What was once manageable weekend work in upkeeping your road turns into a cost and logistic nightmare. Casual fixes are no longer adequate. You can become overwhelmed and frustrated.

Pressure to develop and meet housing demand has resulted in nearly all-season building construction. Contractors eager to get to work and more eager to leave work pound unimproved road surfaces with their vehicles. Since homebuilders primarily use pickup trucks loaded with something heavy, the pounding they dish out exceeds that of most passenger cars that travel at the same speed. This treatment quickly finds areas of weak subgrade. Eventually, road damage occurs in places that you never dreamed would fail.

How Everyday Traffic Damages Unimproved Dirt and Gravel Roadways

➤ Vehicles running in the ditches.

Drivers run into ditches to avoid potholes and evade oncoming traffic. This abuse causes ditches to break down by changing their shape and by filling them with silt and chunks of soil broken away by the slashing action of tires. Once filled, ditches no longer pass water, they hold it. Ponded water in ditchlines eventually permeates the subgrade causing the road surface to soften and pothole.

When cold weather sets-in, moist subgrades may experience frost heave, and then "pump," as the road thaws. In some regions of the country, the term *"frost boil"* is used to describe the action and after effects of soil pumping. Pumping action brings raw mineral soil up from below and onto the running surface. The road usually doesn't heal until the summer sun bakes it solid. By then a depression is formed which worsens with rain. If the ditchline is not maintained, a long lineal planter develops with dense vegetation. Left long enough, wet ditches could be classified as wetlands. In all cases, ditch maintenance becomes more arduous and expensive.

➤ Vehicles running on the roadway shoulders.

Roadways that are either too narrow or lacking sufficient driver visibility get abused when vehicles are driven off the road and onto the adjacent grass or vegetated shoulder. This usually happens because oncoming traffic does not have enough room to safely pass without someone first driving off of the road. The problem is further compounded when four-wheel drive *pilots* look for excuses to go "off road" under the guise of politeness.

If the shoulders are wet and the soil is soft, depressions left by tires will collect rainfall and hold it long enough to allow moisture to seep down and into the road subgrade. Eager to avoid newly formed potholes, traffic migrates *further* into the shoulder area and around the affected area. It's a self-perpetuating problem. Shoulder damage contributes to road deterioration, and worsening road conditions result in yet, broader shoulder damage. Eventually, the shoulder itself becomes a wide, muddy, and rutted extension of the road.

If the road is surfaced with crushed rock, mud and debris dragged from the shoulder and onto the road can contaminate it. Since mud holds water, this area of the roadway may become a prime candidate for future failure. The mud will certainly create dust under dry conditions.

Ruts that regularly appear in the grass or mud off the road's running

Figure 2-3. Lack of curve widening and associated damage.

surface and along the *inside* of a curve usually indicate that the curve is too sharp to handle truck and trailer traffic. In civil engineering terms, this condition is remedied by use of "curve widening," which is a fancy way to say that the roadway is widened in these curved areas to account for wandering trailer wheels and longer vehicles. Damages from lack of curve widening can be seen in Figure 2-3. As you can guess, areas in need of curve widening are prime breeding grounds for potholes and water-filled adventures.

When roads lack curve widening, the solution may be to rake out the ruts, roll and compact the affected area, and place larger sized crushed rock ballast between the edge of road and limit of disturbance. These areas can also be healed by laying fabric or grid over the raked and rolled earth and covering the layer with crushed rock. See the section on fabrics and grids later discussed in Chapter 3.

➤ Rutting, scouring, and tire tracks.

Seepage from road cuts and rainfall can result in channeled water wherever gravity pulls it. If the road is not graded, out-sloped, or crowned, water will travel toward the impressions made from tire tracks. As additional traffic finds the same water-filled tracks, the road's subgrade softens and becomes more susceptible to damage. With slope, tracked water runs and erodes the roadway. This action is called scouring.

Severe and deep scouring can expose large subsurface rocks and instigate slope failure. Water that finds cracks and seams can infiltrate down only to exit somewhere along the road fill slope or stay for the winter, literally. Enough rain can cause the slope to completely shear away from the roadway into a pile of mud.

➤ Vehicle weight.

As discussed earlier, most dirt roads were not built to take the concentrated weight of commercial traffic. If they were, they were built to take it on a temporary basis with scheduled maintenance. Examples of damage-causing commercial vehicles include dump, garbage, and fuel trucks.

If a road has potential weak spots due to organics or wet subgrade, heavy vehicles will find these areas and cause them to fail. Full-sized pickup trucks and vans also contribute significant damage to roads, especially when driven too fast.

Those who are lulled into believing that they can't be damaging a road if they feel no discomfort while pounding across dips and potholes cause grief for neighbors who drive smaller cars. Today's modern suspensions can deceive drivers regarding a road's surface and condition. The dynamic pressure (IMPACT) exerted up and down, with occasional braking distresses unimproved roads and results in rapid roadway deterioration.

➤ Vehicle speed.

Cars, although lighter than pickups, can do as much or more damage as light trucks if driven too fast on dirt roads (Figure 2-4). For one thing, car tires are usually smaller than truck tires. Although smaller, the downward force exerted by a car tire may result in dishing-out a pound per square inch (PSI or pounds per square cm) punishment equal to or greater than a loaded truck tire. Second, cracks and seams that a truck tire would normally bridge may inhale a smaller car's tire thereby helping to transform smaller potholes into bigger holes. Third, smaller speeding tires that rebound and act like a piston can do as much or more damage as slower and heavier truck tires. After all, impact is impact and any downward energy can result in damaged roads.

Speed and braking also pull at the road surface causing mini-waves that jar you every time you drive over them. These mini-waves evolve into familiar "washboards" that rattle any vehicle that travels over them. As a threat to children, pets, and livestock, speed knows no equal, especially when exercised with limited visibility.

As a condition, washboarding is prevalent where vehicles routinely brake, accelerate, and skid. Prime locations for washboarding include intersections, at stop signs, at the top and bottom of hills, bridge locations, and into and out of curves. The curve situation is more related to braking and acceleration as drivers either slow in anticipation of meeting another vehicle or wildly brake and then accelerate in reaction to what's coming at them through the curve.

➤ Wet and cold season use.

As summer turns to fall and fall welcomes winter, the potential for road damage increases. Wetter periods of autumn, winter, and spring soften roads thereby exposing them to rapid deterioration and damage when traveled upon. Latitudes extreme from the equator and higher altitude properties are liable to experience extreme cold and severe weather. Frost protection in the form of road shaping, grading, surfacing, and drainage all become critical items to preserving roads in ultra-cold regions. Some locations encountering annual freeze depths of four feet (120 cm) or more require extraordinary maintenance and demanding repair schedules. Vehicle impact during such conditions accelerates road damage and repair costs mount.

Winter also affords increased opportunities for multiple freeze-and-thaw cycles. Although freeze depths may only extend a few inches or so into the ground, these occurrences break up roads by heaving wet subgrade soils to the surface and forming potholes. As traffic beats this partially frozen mixture down, the resulting depression holds more water. Continued traffic never allows the depression to heal until, ultimately, a seasonal change brings enough light and warmth to the road causing it to dry and solidify. The result is a mean and permanent pothole. A constant reminder of Ol' Man Winter.

➤ Varying vibration amplitudes and vehicle cycles.

Wow, what a topic! In the world of pure physics where people live in white laboratory coats, we have discovered that all vehicles transmit a vibration and motion wave into the roadway they travel upon.

The "motion wave" that each vehicle transmits is a product of that vehicle's suspension and stiffness, weight, speed, tire size, distance between axles, and distance between wheels. If large, off-road mining trucks or construction scrapers were to regularly travel down public roadways with everyday traffic at everyday speeds, the roadway would soon begin to show a pattern of stress and severe failure. In a normal street vehicle, you would experience this damage as a wild and loping ride as opposed to the smooth even cruising that we all expect on public highways.

Another problem involves roadways that are already built with a lope or vibratory frequency already formed into the grade. This results from poor construction techniques where the contractor's trucks or road graders bounced a little too much while working the road. In the case of road grader equipment, minute adjustments in blade angle can result in a poorly graded and loping roadway. Although not easily visible to the eye, undulating roadways worsen as vehicles of varying size and weight bounce over the road's "waves" culminating in surface deterioration.

Other elements imposed by heavy equipment such as traveling too fast, running on worn tires, having bent rims, and exceeding highway load limits all contribute to "motion cycles." If your contractor is using

Weight and Speed Damages Roads

Light Weight Vehicles Traveling Fast	Heavier Vehicles Traveling at Moderate Speed	Heaviest Vehicles Traveling Slow

Fast moving, light weight vehicles can cause as much or more damage to roads as heavier and slower moving vehicles. Although lighter in weight, small vehicle tires may transfer greater pressure per square foot into a road's surface than tires from larger and heavier vehicles. Speed works to increase impact, decrease safety, and expand road damage.

The motto for preserving roads is:

"Slow Down"

Figure 2-4. Weight and speed.

construction vehicles that are not licensed for public highway use, they may be classified as off-road vehicles. Such vehicles can ruin your road in short order if allowed to freely travel upon it.

Cheap and Quick Fixes

It is cheaper to fix your road once than it is to continually fix your cars over time. However, your resources and timing may dictate that a temporary fix is the right thing for you—now.

Here are some quick fixes that may provide you a temporary reprieve from full restoration. At worst, they will aid in retarding additional road damage. At best, they may improve some sections of your roadway beyond your wildest expectations:

➤ Direct traffic by installing standard-sized signage.

Invest in regulation-sized signage that depicts roadway conditions. Be sure to install these signs on heavy, treated posts at regulation height. To determine what regulation height is, check with your local authorities or sign distributor.

Signs warn tourists, land buyers, and visitors of what to expect. Properly displayed signs can indicate that people may be watching—people who care about traffic safety, roadway-use practice, and crime prevention.

They suggest an appearance of law and order to those who have a tendency to speed, drive with reckless abandon, or who care little about endangering you, your family, and neighbors.

Strategic signage can include the following: *speed limits, children present, bus stop, curve ahead, use turnout, horse or animal crossing,* etc. Use of *dead end* signs will automatically reduce traffic volume where access is limited or where people want to lessen unwanted traffic.

➤ Fix (and maintain!) ditches.

Re-establish ditch lines with shovels or by using heavy grading equipment. If a ditch never existed where one is required, establish one. Refer to the ditches and road conditions in Figure 2-5. Be sure that any ditched water has a place to go *away* from the road subgrade. This may mean ditching the water into an adjacent field, into a forested area, or maybe into a pipe that extends under your roadway, away from the subgrade.

Ditching keeps subgrades dry and provides a location for surface water drainage during rainfall and snowmelt. Work to remove branches and leaves that may clog or degrade your ditches.

In order to reduce erosion potential and stay ahead of native weeds, plant native grasses in the ditch and over-seed at least once a year. Grass and controlled vegetation can be aesthetically pleasing as they work to bio-filtrate ditch water. Bio-filtration is a natural process that aids in the removal of phosphorus and larger suspended particles commonly found in roadway runoff, which adversely affects water quality.

Ditchlines and Road Surfacing
Not To Scale

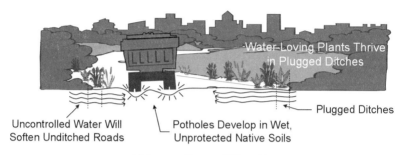

Water-Loving Plants Thrive in Plugged Ditches

Plugged Ditches

Uncontrolled Water Will
Soften Unditched Roads

Potholes Develop in Wet,
Unprotected Native Soils

Worse Case Situation

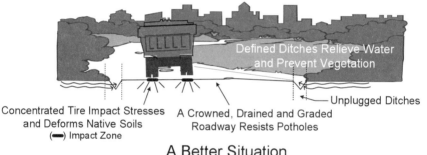

Defined Ditches Relieve Water
and Prevent Vegetation

Unplugged Ditches

Concentrated Tire Impact Stresses
and Deforms Native Soils
(➡) Impact Zone

A Crowned, Drained and Graded
Roadway Resists Potholes

A Better Situation

Crushed Rock Surfacing
Crushed Base Rock

Defined Ditches

With Rock Surfacing, Tire Impact is
Spread Over a Larger Area
(➡) Impact Zone

Mechanically Compacted, Rolled,
and Graded Native Subgrade

The Best Situation

Figure 2-5. Ditchlines and road surfacing.

Ideally, ditches should be cut and side-sloped no steeper than three feet (90 cm) horizontal for every one foot (30 cm) of vertical. This of course depends upon the amount of available right-of-way or land that you have to work with. However as a rule, flatter sideslopes result in easier maintenance and enhanced slope stability. Ditches that are cut vertical with minimal slope can be hazardous and always pose a risk to those driving during icy, foggy, or snowy conditions.

In some cases, you may elect to narrow down a portion of the roadway itself in exchange for the room required to establish wider and better ditches. Any roadway stabilization that results from ditching is usually worth the sacrifice in less adjoining road width, however, narrow roads and wide ditchlines can be a prescription for vehicles driving into the ditch.

Significant digging and road damage follows vehicles that wander into ditchlines and cannot easily back out, get stuck, or become high-centered. This almost always results in carved ruts and grooves where the vehicle has been dug out or dragged to safety. The benefits of poorly placed and constructed ditches may not be worth the problems and costs associated with repeated vehicle intrusion, trench destruction, and compromised safety. It certainly does nothing for improved neighborly relations.

➤ Check the cross culverts and pipes.

All pipes and culverts installed under your roadway provide one purpose; to convey or move water across and under your road. Water may come from the ditchline, a pond outlet, or even a stream. In any case, since water falls with gravity and gravity is dictated by terrain, culverts and pipes help to move water in the direction water would naturally take. The difference is that you are conveying this water on your terms, away from the roadway.

If you need culverts and don't have any, install them or any other cross piping where it is needed. Also check to be sure that all existing culverts are operating clear of debris and dirt. You should easily be able to see the circular hole of light on the other side of the culvert. If you cannot see light from the other end of the pipe, it may be too small in diameter, it may be plugged with debris, or the pipe may have failed somewhere under the roadway.

Debris can be pulled away from pipe openings (Figure 2-6) and material within the culvert can be cleaned manually. Vacuum trucks are also equipped to perform this task. Other creative solutions include lashing up winches, cables, and using high-pressure water. Spelunking and pipe slithering may appear intriguing however such adventures *are not* recommended and may threaten your life. Don't do it, besides, you don't know what you may meet down there.

Sometimes culverts leak. Water is observed going in the upper end and nothing comes out the lower end. Corrugated, nonaluminum metal culverts are notorious for corroding over long periods of time resulting in leaks and weakened support. To determine the problem, a remote

Figure 2-6. A clogged and soon-to-be vegetated culvert.

Figure 2-7. Crushed culvert end.

camera can be pulled through the pipe in order to confirm the degree of deterioration. Upon determining that the metal culvert needs replacement, you can choose to open cut and install a new pipe or line the existing shell with a PVC pipeliner. Liner treatments have proven to be a cheap and easy solution to total pipe replacement provided that the repaired pipe retains sufficient water carrying capacity to still do the job. Inadequate pipes that cannot handle water volumes should be replaced or augmented with additional piping. Your only option with crushed pipes, as shown in Figure 2-7, is to replace them.

Once your culverts are clean, trash racks can be installed to prevent future debris and larger animals from entering them.

➤ Crown and grade the road surface.

You can immediately improve your road by grading all surface drainage lateral to ditchlines from road centerline as shown in Figure 2-8. This will shed moisture and rainfall quickly away from where it can do the most damage. Grading also removes surface irregularities resulting in a smoother, more predictable roadway.

It is highly recommended that when grading your roadway, you roll

Roadway Surfaces and Drainage
Not to Scale

Broken and Beaten Down Roadway Surfaces

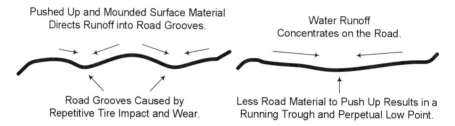

Pushed Up and Mounded Surface Material Directs Runoff into Road Grooves.

Water Runoff Concentrates on the Road.

Road Grooves Caused by Repetitive Tire Impact and Wear.

Less Road Material to Push Up Results in a Running Trough and Perpetual Low Point.

Stable and Well-Drained Roadway Surfaces

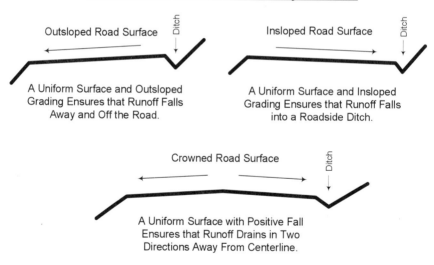

Outsloped Road Surface   Ditch

Insloped Road Surface   Ditch

A Uniform Surface and Outsloped Grading Ensures that Runoff Falls Away and Off the Road.

A Uniform Surface and Insloped Grading Ensures that Runoff Falls into a Roadside Ditch.

Crowned Road Surface   Ditch

A Uniform Surface with Positive Fall Ensures that Runoff Drains in Two Directions Away From Centerline.

Figure 2-8. Surfaces and drainage.

and compact the road's surface at the same time. Consider renting or hiring a heavy, static (nonvibratory) rolling machine. Rolling minimizes the
road's micro-surface area, reduces the size of air voids in the soil, and
results in less moisture-holding capacity. Smooth and dry road surfaces
also perform in resisting traffic impact and wheel loading.

➤ Fix potholes quickly and correctly.

Potholes are a nuisance. They work to destroy your car while fraying
your nerves. Potholes that you have tried to fill yet continually recur in
the same location, year after year, are telling you something. They are
telling you that there is something at that location that needs to be excavated out and replaced with more stable material. Chronic potholes
may also be telling you that the road needs drainage control, improved
surfacing, altered geometry, or maybe a change in driving habits.

• Ditching.

If your road is not adequately ditched adjacent to chronic potholes,
try ditching before excavation and filling (see Figure 2-9). Ditching will
channel water away from your pothole problem and this will definitely
improve your road's performance. In fact, it may improve enough to
minimize or entirely avoid the cost of pothole repairs at that location.
Give it a try.

• Excavation.

If however, the affected stretch of roadway is already properly ditched
and water is not permeating the subgrade, plan to excavate and fill the
potholes with free-draining structural material or preferably, crushed rock.

Begin by excavating out the pothole area. Remove all damp and wet
dirt and any organic material that you find. Be sure to also remove any
roots, sticks, and stump materials that protrude into the pothole or else
you may be back re-excavating an adjacent pothole next to the one that
you're currently fixing. Depending on the number of holes, the hardness

of the roadway, or your available resources, excavation may be accomplished by hand or by using a digging machine such as a backhoe.

- **Refill the Hole.**

Replace all road material removed (sometimes called spoils) with two- to four-inch sized crushed rock or with dry granular material sometimes called "pit-run." These products can usually be found at a local gravel pit or construction supply yard.

In choosing between rock or pit-run, your first consideration should be availability. If both products are available, crushed rock works better in fine-grained soils, where there is moisture, and in wet climates. Pit-run works well with compatible coarser soils and in drier locations. Softer subgrade material should be first topped with fabric or with four-inch (10 cm) sized or larger crushed rock before smaller crushed rock or pit-run is added above it. If you're in doubt, it's hard to go wrong filling excavated potholes 100 percent with crushed rock.

If you install two- to four-inch (5 cm–10 cm) sized crushed rock in the bottom of the hole, consider placing a second layer of one-inch (25 mm) minus sized rock over it in order to fill voids and gain a smoother road surface. Mound the last layer and allow traffic to slowly compact it in place. When the mound ceases to settle, you can shave it even with the road's surface or just leave as is. DO NOT, however, leave a depression that will collect water or allow traffic to bottom out.

Pit-run works well in helping to bind larger crushed rock and fill voids. Of course, potholes not allowed to drain, or which are not sealed from moisture, will continue to cause problems even if filled with rock. This happens because crushed rock still allows water to infiltrate and sit in the pothole. If the pothole is near the roadway edge, one alternative is to dig a narrow channel allowing potholed water to exit laterally. Then backfill and seal off the pothole.

Surfaces of larger potholes can be filled, compacted, and sealed with a topping of crushed rock mixed with impermeable soil. Fine-grained, in-organic soils such as clay, silt, and till work well for sealing potholes from

Figure 2-9. Vegetation-filled ditches and potholes.

future water infiltration. This strategy improves the odds of keeping future water out of repaired potholes, however; clays and silts must be used with discretion. In this application, they are only being used to shield water. Not provide structural support or stability. A few inches of impermeable material graded into the pothole's surface should suffice.

Sometimes, even though you use the correct type of crushed rock to fill potholes, the rock won't stay put. Vehicles traveling too fast are one reason why crushed rock works its way out of holes. Another reason relates to the road's hardness. Hard-packed dirt roads can be tough to penetrate for even the sharpest crushed rock. When this happens, deeper potholes may need to be scarified in order to accept and hold crushed rock. Shallower potholes may need to be overexcavated in order to "soften" and deepen the hole to better grip and bind crushed rock. Speaking of binding, adding minor amounts of fine-grained, inorganic soils such as clay, silt, and till to crushed rock may help fill voids and in doing so, seat it in place.

One last word concerning size of crushed rock. Crushed rock size must be commensurate with depth of hole. You wouldn't use four-inch

(10 cm) rock in a hole three inches (8 mm) deep nor would you consider filling a four-foot (120 cm) deep hole with ⅜-inch (10 mm) sized crushed rock unless the rock was free, in great abundance, or your only alternative. There are better and more effective techniques for repairing potholes.

- **Rock restrictions.**

As a rule, do not use rounded rock such as washed drainfield rock, pebbles, pea gravel, or river rock on roadway surfaces. Round rock spits, turns, and spins when exposed to traffic and it is always liable to go airborne. When applied to potholes, it's just a matter of time before round rock shuffles itself out of the hole and into the ditchline. This rule is true for rounded rock regardless of rock size.

Occasionally, washed or large round rock can be found cheap. In this case, restrict its use to areas deep in the bottom of potholes. In similar fashion to chunk concrete and asphalt, large round rock may, under certain conditions, work as deep roadway ballast. When used as deep ballast in potholes, cover and seat it with adequate crushed rock or pit-run. A properly placed and bound mat of large rounded rock can work to support

Figure 2-10. Ragged transition between paving and dirt.

additional layers or courses of smaller crushed rock placed above it.

When dealing with round rock, seat it firmly so that it has no way to move or torque its way out of the hole. Even in deep fills, use of round rock in roadway restoration is suspect to failure on account of it's rolling potential when under stress.

- **Another tip.**

When you are dealing with relatively smooth or "flat" road surfaces, the best way to locate those low spots and dips is after a good rain. Water and puddles reveal those areas that need filling or repair.

➤ Match grades where low areas exist.

Protect road surfaces by bringing low areas up level and even with pavement and running lanes. Figure 2-10 shows a ragged road edge between pavement and dirt. Figure 2-11 shows pavement damage resulting from vehicles rolling up onto and off of a road's edge.

➤ Only repair the running lanes.

On narrow roadways, you can save time and money by only repairing the running lanes. Ignore the middle of the roadway as well as the shoulder areas outside of the running lanes.

Altering Driving Patterns to Reduce Roadway Damage

If your damaged roadway could talk, it would plead "tread lightly on me." Listen to it and work to arrest all on-going damage. You can accomplish this first and foremost by driving slowly, slowing others down, and staying out of the ditches. Be sure to give clear warning to any trucks and cars coming from or leaving your property *to do the same.* Keep your vehicle on the road, clear the ditches by hand, and fill any potholes with rocks until actual construction begins. It is always a good idea to try to control the manner in which others abuse a road until restoration commences. This at least warms them up for changes that you and your road association are

Figure 2-11. Pavement edge damage and low shoulders.

trying to incorporate.

Another effective strategy is to compile a map of your roadway. On the map, note areas of degradation and damage as well as new and proposed signage with speed limits. Include all driveways and new turnout areas on this map. Also include a brief plan for restoration and provide an approximate cost of repairs that the road association or neighbors plan on spending.

Send this map and summary information to all companies that frequently travel your roadway such as Federal Express, the U.S. Postal Service, UPS, the pizza deliveryman, the garbage collector, oil and gas delivery trucks, and utility meter readers. This action will get their notice and they will usually respond positively. They want to be liked and they want your business. The result should be less abuse and speeding over your neighborhood roadways. Those who do not comply can be leveraged through calls to upper management.

✓ More "Do's"

- Use a level to check all ditchlines.

- Mound pothole fills higher than the road surface.

- Only expect temporary relief from short-term fixes.

- Read your road's characteristics after a good rainfall.

- Enter into road repair work with clearly defined goals.

- Look for indicators that reveal why your road is failing.

- Understand that speed and weight can do equal damage.

- Make sure that pipes and culverts are working correctly.

- Learn about the vegetation and soils along your roadway.

- Get water to drain off your roadway as quickly as possible.

- Use only crushed rock for base course and running surfaces.

- Erect road signage as a cheap way to educate the uneducated.

- Consider quick fixes only as a means to permanent restoration.

- Walk the roadway and develop an on-ground perspective for it.

- Understand that if it's organic and it's in your roadway, it's bad.

- Only invest in paving after you've invested in a suitable roadbed.

- Compact any material that you place under or over your roadway.

- Find a road location or willing neighbor who can take waste road dirt.

- Pick up some roadway dirt and determine if it's fine or coarse grained.

- Determine the absolute minimum amount of repair work required and do it.

- Ponder the effect that connecting driveways and side roads has upon your road.

- Send all delivery services a road map explaining the rules of driving on your road.

- Expect potholes and patches repaired during cold and wet weather to be less durable than those repaired under warm and dry conditions.

CHAPTER 3

The Mechanics of Permanently Restoring Unimproved Roadways

Whether you do the work yourself or contract it out, road repairs usually follow a sequence of events. Let's review the mechanics common to road repair beginning with procedures and sequencing.

Construction Procedures for Restoring and Rebuilding Damaged Roadways

There are many elements to consider when preparing to restore or construct a private road and they all can affect your sequence of construction. Note Figure 3-1, the construction-sequencing flowchart. Then, consider at least the following as it pertains to your project:

- Will you impact waterways?
- What type of soils are you dealing with?
- What time of year do you plan on doing restoration work?
- Where is your project located and who are your suppliers?
- What erosion control and safety measures will be required?
- How will your project impact traffic and adjoining property?
- Is your project in close proximity to sensitive areas including wetlands?

- What is your project's magnitude and what level of restoration do you desire?

- Will any permits be required? What special provisions or permit conditions should you prepare for in order to obtain final plan approval?

Typical Roadway Construction Sequencing

1. Contact all roadway users and, if necessary, set up detour signage.

It is recommended that all people living on the road be contacted well in advance of construction. Give all association members and neighbors a written schedule describing each planned construction phase, a map showing all work and detour signage, and include a menu of project milestone and completion dates.

2. Call or have your contractor call the 1-800 utility locate number (One-Call System) at least two days prior to commencing work.

Before breaking ground, all below-ground wet and dry utilities must be clearly located. Dry utilities include power, gas, telephone, cable, and data systems. Wet utilities include sanitary, storm, and water lines. Those companies who own, operate, and maintain these utilities will mark them on request or will contract this work out to a utility locate service.

A strict color code format exists that assigns a paint color for each type of utility. The utility companies will actually paint dashed lines on the ground directly above where they believe its facilities exist. Call your local municipality, power or gas company for the details in your area or rely on your contractor to perform this task, but do not miss this step of the process. (For more information on the one-call process, see Chapter 7, Common Pitfalls to Avoid.)

Unpaved Restoration Sequencing & Cost Comparison

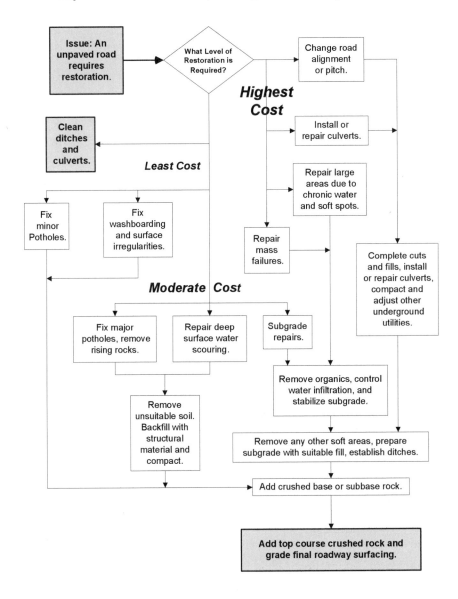

Figure 3-1. Unpaved road construction sequencing.

3. Install all erosion control items.

If conditions or a permit warrants the use of erosion control devices such as silt fence, straw bales, or orange protective fencing, the time to install it is before any logging, clearing, or earthwork commences.

4. Begin with the deepest work.

In roadways, culverts are usually the deepest item. Begin the process by cleaning all culverts and pipes. Restore and repair them to proper working order. If required, add culverts or remove and replace those that have failed. Channels into and out of these culverts must be cleaned and cleared of silt and debris. Inspect pipe inlets and outlets for erosion or void formation. If damages due to flowing water are observed, plate these areas with large rock. Your goal is to neutralize the destructive action of running water that enters and exits your culverts. Any existing concrete storm structures should also be cleaned and checked for proper operation.

During excavation, you may encounter various underground utility lines. Hopefully, you've used the One-Call System *and,* for double insurance, also called local utility companies to inform them of your work. By doing so, you'll have an idea of what to expect and they'll have a chance to either pre-mark utilities or inspect your project once you're underway. Most utility companies will be interested to know your scope of work and schedule for construction. They will probably show up sometime during the project. Besides, if something under your control goes wrong, informed utility companies tend to be more sympathetic than those companies whom you have neglected to inform.

Treat all utility lines with care. Stockpile adequate materials for shoring and support should you undermine a utility line or cause one to become unstable. Any utility lines that you unexpectedly encounter should be photographed, measured, field located, and documented to the best of your ability. It's a good idea to have the phone numbers of all known utility purveyors on hand and in the field so that if you do get into a jam, break something, or reach a stalemate, they can be called in to provide guidance and assistance.

5. Fix chronic potholes and get rid of unsuitable waste soils.

Repaired potholes can indicate a larger problem of subgrade degeneration and usually the presence of moisture. In fixing potholes, there are few alternatives and fewer correct ones.

As discussed earlier in this book, potholes should be excavated of all unsuitable (rotten) and wet soil and then backfilled with granular material such as pit-run or crushed rock. After fixing your potholes, the excavated material should either be wasted in adjacent areas or hauled away. Any organic material still visible in and around the excavation must be removed as part of the excavation or during final grading.

In addition to large crushed rock, consider using bulk waste material such as chunks of broken bedrock, concrete, and asphalt when repairing stubborn and deep potholes. Sizes of chunk material vary but it's safe to assume that if the hole is big enough and they fit flat, they'll probably work fine. Although classified as unsuitable by some public agencies, if placed with care, chunk materials can work wonders in the deeper layers of a pothole or road fill. Chunk concrete and asphalt act to float and support fill material. The trick is to lay the material flat, compact it in place, and completely fill all voids under and around the chunks.

Chunk material can sometimes be used to effectively bridge bogs and holes of wet organic soils in lieu of costly soil excavation and fill replacement. Many solid roads have been built over wet conditions using this technique. Best of all, chunk material is usually free or cheap to obtain. An excellent source of chunk material is broken and excess flat concrete roof tile. Fractured concrete roof tile works well when used to stabilize and fill potholes. It can be easily broken and tailored to the size of each hole and should be bound with small-sized crushed rock or quality pit-run. Check with local roofers and suppliers for availability. They may be glad to give you all you want and possibly even deliver it, free of charge.

Chunk material fills must be thought out beforehand, and systematically placed. Also check with your public agencies to determine if use of such material is allowed. Some agencies frown upon or completely prohibit the use of chunk asphalt and concrete in fills.

Road fills can also be constructed from recycled materials including crushed glass, ground tires (crumb rubber), fly ash, brick, and foam products. Each material has its advantages and disadvantages. After researching each alternative, you may choose to employ these materials or other exotics in your project.

6. Shape and grade the existing surface material.

If the entire roadway is in need of restoration, the roadway should be ripped to a depth of four to eight inches (10 cm to 20 cm). The depth of ripping depends on the integrity of the base road material in question. Ripping is performed by using either a bulldozer or road grader that is equipped with "ripper teeth" or, in shorter road sections, by using a backhoe or excavator that is equipped with "ripper teeth" on the bucket.

As a word of caution, it may be cheaper to perform this work with a bulldozer or road grader if:

- The roadway area to be treated is relatively large.
- The bulldozer can be used for multiple duties such as in grading and ditch work.

➤ Ripping the road's surface accomplishes the following during restoration:

- It dries out the roadway's surface material.
- It prelevels the road surface and makes it easier to grade.
- It redistributes the material that is available for grading.
- It induces larger rock and organics such as limbs and stumps to the surface for collection, disposal, or reuse.
- It helps to remove "memory" from the road surface including areas of continual washboarding, dips, and humps.
- It prepares the road base for adding and "knitting" in new

material in the event you are building a crown or adding additional layers of rock.

7. Roll and compact the road subgrade material.

After the surface is ripped, the loose material should be graded and roll-compacted while in place, similar to the way you would roll a new lawn after seeding and raking. The primary difference in using this analogy is that road reconstruction projects are just bigger and more costly.

Roll the grade with an operator-driven static drum compactor. Rolling in this manner will help to eliminate future weak spots of unconsolidated material. Rolling will also assist in forcing new material into the road's surface. This works toward creating flat running surfaces that shed water. When working raw subgrade, the objective is to create uniform, smooth, and firm surfaces upon which fabric or crushed subbase rock can later be placed. Rolling and compaction are dry weather activities and may require moisture to be added to the subgrade in order to attain optimal results.

8. Place subbase rock or geotextiles over native subgrade.

At this point, it is your choice to use either a crushed rock base, or first place fabric or grid over the exposed compacted subgrade, and then rock above it. Why add rock and fabric to improve roadways?

➤ Building up roads with stable nonorganic material accomplishes the following benefits in improving your road's health:

- It provides traction.
- It helps to reduce dust.
- It prepares the road for possible future hard surfacing.
- It separates the running surface from soil contamination and any below grade moisture problems.

Structural Benefit of Using Crushed Rock Surfacing
Not To Scale

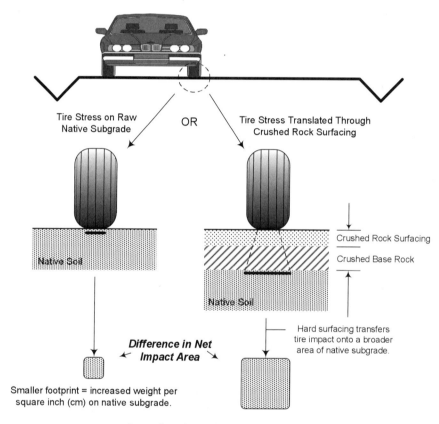

Tire Stress on Raw
Native Subgrade

OR

Tire Stress Translated Through
Crushed Rock Surfacing

Crushed Rock Surfacing

Crushed Base Rock

Native Soil

Native Soil

*Difference in Net
Impact Area*

Hard surfacing transfers
tire impact onto a broader
area of native subgrade.

Smaller footprint = increased weight per
square inch (cm) on native subgrade.

Larger footprint = decreased weight per square inch (cm) impact
on native subgrade resulting in less soil stress and potential damage.
(Use of fabric or grid will yield even greater reductions in road Impact.)

Figure 3-2. Load distribution relative to thickness of crushed rock.

Examples of Typical Road Sections
Not to Scale

NOTE: Thickness of crushed rock, hard surfacing, and type of geotextiles used, depends upon many factors including soil type, soil strength, moisture conditions, and expected loading. Seek professional engineering or geotechnical advise before specifying materials and quantities.

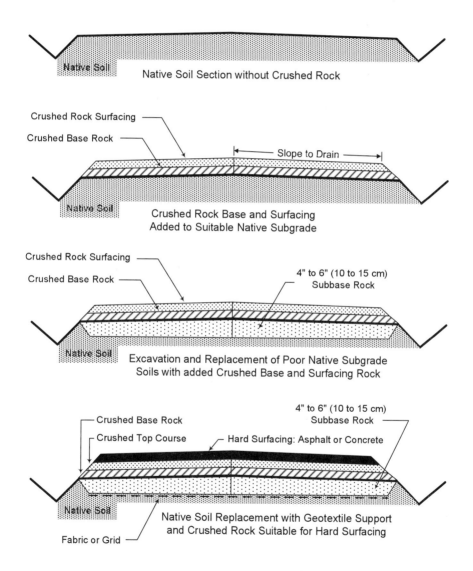

Figure 3-3. Road sections.

- It distributes vehicle tire loading over a broader area. This is achieved by adding varying layers of fabric, structural fill, crushed rock, or hard surfacing. The thicker the structural section, the greater the load distribution. See Figure 3-2.

- It helps to build-up the subgrade thereby raising the running surface above adjacent ditches and shoulders.

Two primary means of building unsurfaced roadways above compacted subgrade involve the use of crushed rock alone or in concert with a geotextile (fabric or grid). At this time, notice the road sections shown on Figure 3-3. Together, crushed rock and geotextiles complement each other. Crushed rock can be used effectively on its own; however, fabric or grid rarely can be effective without use of crushed rock above or below them. Let's explore these products.

➤ Crushed rock subbase.

Crushed rock subbase should be applied in lifts no thinner than four inches (10 cm). Six inches (15 cm) of rock are preferred and more is usually better depending upon native soil conditions and whether or not you use fabric or grid below the rock. After adding rock to the roadway, it should be graded and rolled with an operator-driven static drum compactor.

If your subbase is sound, hard, and dry, a vibratory compactor may be used; however, it should be used sparingly until you are certain that it is not drawing water up and into your subgrade.

Depending on its availability, subbase rock by definition is generally larger crushed rock and can range between two and eight inches (5 cm and 20 cm). The size of rock you choose should depend on how soft the subgrade is and the number of layers of smaller rock you can afford to place above it. As a rule, when building roads with crushed rock, rock size diminishes as you build the road grade up from native earth to final surfacing.

If your road is to be used for logging, heavy hauling, or off road construction access, the amount of subbase rock should be increased to a depth of at least eight inches (20 cm) or more depending upon whatever depth the rock ceases to sink and becomes stabilized.

The tradeoff in using larger rock is that it tends to finish as a coarser running surface and it's tougher to grade. This can damage tires and result in rougher riding conditions. If you desire a smooth running surface suitable for passenger cars, you'll need to place additional smaller crushed rock above larger subbase rock.

As you can see, it takes a significant amount of rock to properly build a structural roadway that will stand the test of time. The good news is that quality road building results in a road that only needs to be built once!

Reliance on rock alone is also somewhat risky. If the soil subgrade is not prepared well enough to prevent rock contamination and penetration, rock will become dirty and quite a bit of it will disappear and be wasted into the subgrade. If the subgrade is wet and deep in organics, there can be no end to the amount of rock that will be pushed down deep into the soil.

As this rock sinks deeper into the earth, a zone of failure will begin to form on the road surface culminating in a low spot or depression. Sinking rock is slowly displaced with wet and unstable soils that concurrently rise up and engulf it. This kneading of soils displaces your rock investment with material that is causing your problem in the first place. *It is exactly what you do not want.* Wet unstable soils surfacing and settling onto the road running surface, again.

Given enough time and traffic, the road in this spot will turn to mud when it rains and dust when it dries, completely hiding any trace of your original rock. Soon, you'll witness the birth of a pothole and the joys that they bring.

Adding untold layers of rock until a road stabilizes is costly, time consuming, and unpredictable. There is an alternative to mass dumping of rock into weak roadway subgrades. The alternatives are geosynthetics and geotextiles, more commonly called fabrics and grids. Without these materials, your investment in multiple layers of rock, additional excavation, and extended work schedule can be excessive and, certainly, stress your budget.

➤ Fabrics and grids.

How do you think roadways are usually constructed across miles of frozen tundra, wet bogs, and very poor soils without tremendous excavation activity? Many are built using engineered fabrics and grids. Engineered fabrics and grids help to "bridge" poor, wet soils thereby resulting in less expensive construction and minimal environmental impact. Use of engineered fabrics and grids to restore very poor roadways reduces the need to overexcavate and replace poor soils with mountains of rock and nonorganic structural material.

• Less excavation, less cost.

Fabrics and grid provide an avenue to minimize or perhaps even avoid, subgrade overexcavation. In road construction, you're usually exposed to three distinct cost centers related to excavation.

1. The first cost center is the cost to excavate and remove material. These costs escalate if you cannot dump excavated spoils and material locally or within short trucking distance. Your situation worsens if your material is so poor that it can only be accepted at some remote and high-priced dumpsite.

2. The second cost center involves hauling in and placing an equal amount of better material in order to bring the roadway up to grade.

3. A third cost center is schedule. A longer schedule means more overhead, increased stand-by equipment costs, and the extended risk of encountering poor weather.

Your exposure to weather-related cost overruns can be enormous. Excavations are holes and holes hold water. If it rains on your excavation and otherwise marginal but acceptable soil becomes wet and unusable, you have two choices. Either pay your contractor to shut down, pump the hole of water, and reimburse him throughout the work stoppage, or continue onward by removing spoiled material and replacing it with imported dry suitable fill or rock. Both alternatives hit your pocketbook coming and going and neither choice is appealing.

Although situations do exist where the subgrade soil is so poor that some excavation and soil replacement is unavoidable, today's engineered fabrics and grids have been designed to sharply reduce the need for wholesale, automatic excavation and fill replacement. And, they increase your ability to stay on schedule.

Consider the use of engineered fabrics and grids in order to save money, expedite work, and build a better roadway. These products are relatively cheap, they're easy to install, and they last forever. Fabrics and grids are available in rolls of varying widths and thicknesses.

• **Easy installation and other benefits.**

How often have you added rock to the roadway just to see it disappear? Where did it go? If it wasn't tossed off the roadway by spinning tires, it was probably pushed down into the roadway as previously discussed. Without some form of barrier preventing raw earth from swallowing your rock, most rock placed over areas of poor subgrade can and will disappear over a period of months. To a great extent, fabrics and grid work to keep soft silts and clays from displacing and contaminating clean, crushed roadway rock.

Engineered fabric and grids also work to spread and evenly distribute the punishing impact exerted by tires traveling over the roadway. While spreading impact over a broader area of subgrade, fabric and grid work to keep tires off sensitive soils. This results in less pounding on raw soil and helps to preserve the road's foundational support.

• **Product and application.**

Although fabrics and grids offer some benefit when used to "bridge" potholes, they are most effective when installed over entire road sections before adding successive layers of crushed rock base or pit-run material.

Fabric and grid come in a variety of materials, weights, and sizes. There are many manufacturers, each offering variations of fabric and grid designed for specific applications, soil types, and loading. With your neighbor's help, these products can easily be rolled out over prepared subgrade prior to placing rock.

Depending on the road's native material and shape of prism, it may be beneficial to dig the edges of the fabric or grid into the subgrade. This process is called "keying." The fabric or grid must be wrinkle-free and should overlap on the edges and ends according to the manufacturer's recommendation.

Speak with a supplier, civil engineer, or geotechnical consultant in your area before costing out and deciding which type of fabric or grid you'll use. Study the materials and make your decision based on cost, anticipated fill material, traffic loading, and subgrade conditions. Your contractor may also be knowledgeable about these techniques and offer suggestions concerning your needs and local success with varying products. Manufacturers and suppliers can be found in the yellow pages under "construction materials."

9. Place an intermediary layer of crushed rock.

Whether you choose to use fabric, grid, or a large crushed rock subbase, the next step is to add a layer of intermediary rock. This layer of rock should be 1¼ inch to 1 inch (30 mm to 25 mm) "minus" in size. The minus means that the crushed rock mix will contain a wide range of material sizes not exceeding 1¼ to 1 inch (30 mm to 25 mm) on the large end and small enough to *theoretically* be size zero on the small end. A large component of this rock as specified will also include a percentage of smaller rock, sand, and perhaps silt or clay.

Crushed rock mixes can also be labeled "clean," meaning that the rock meets a tighter range of sizes than an equivalently labeled "minus" mix. A 1¼ inch (30 mm) clean mix will not exceed 1¼ inches (30 mm) on the large end and may contain nothing smaller than ⅝ of an inch (16 mm) on the small end. A clean mix will pass water easier than a minus mix, however, a minus mix will pack better than a clean mix. They both have their place in the scheme of things.

Above all, crushed rock mixes should match those commonly used and specified for construction by your local permit agency. If the mix is good enough as an approved state or municipal product, it is good enough for your road.

You want this layer of rock to bind tightly while providing fill characteristics required for strength and uniformity. In the case of adding intermediary rock above subbase rock, intermediary rock acts as a binder and finer course of material. Over fabric or grid, intermediary rock serves as a stable and solid layer between the fabric or grid below and the final running course above. The requirement with grid is that the intermediary rock be sufficiently small to interlock with the grid's webbing thereby forming a structural mat within you roadway.

Depth of rock again depends on the condition of the subgrade material, thickness of subbase, or weight of fabric or grid used. It also depends on expected traffic volumes, traffic speed, and anticipated types of vehicles that will be using the road. Naturally, your budget is also a major consideration. As always, the thicker it is applied, the better. As a rule, intermediary rock above subbase or fabric should be applied to a thickness of *no less* than three to four inches (8 cm to 10 cm). Similar to subbase, the preferred depth of rock is usually six inches (15 cm) or greater.

10. Give your budget a breather while allowing your new road time to perform.

At this point, it is possible to drive on the road and evaluate your work. If you live in northern or higher elevation climates, it is a good idea to run over the road for a winter. Test it. Give it a chance to fail, to see if it sheds water and if it can handle traffic during adverse-weather conditions. Do any depressions and weak spots emerge? Freeze and thaw conditions also quickly expose water and subgrade deficiencies. Before proceeding, you will want to know how sound your roadway is.

Most people view this portion of the process and the money spent as a yearly budget break-even point from which next year's budget and planning can begin, and rightly so. Owners following this process will develop a sense of accomplishment and enjoy the fact that they have invested wisely in their roadway. Everyone needs confidence that his money and time are not being wasted.

If weaknesses are evident or areas of the road appear to be underconstructed or even missed, they can be targeted for future repair. Roads that prove sturdy and ready for final rock can be finished with confidence during the next work cycle.

11. Apply the final running course of crushed rock.

When you have allowed ample time for the road to accept everyday traffic, rain, freezing, thawing, heat, and settling, any minor dips and depressions should be properly filled and graded out. Ample time to test a roadway can be anywhere from three months to a year depending on where you live, traffic loading, and weather.

The final running course of crushed rock should now be applied to the road surface. This final course of rock can be either $^3/_8$-inch or $^5/_8$-inch (10 mm or 16 mm) minus crushed rock. The final topping should be applied at a depth of *no less* than two inches (5 cm). Usual depth of final running course on public roads is approximately four inches (10 cm). Once this type of rock sets up, it can appear as hard as concrete.

With proper grading and compaction, the smaller rock will fill voids within the surface of the intermediary course and work to bind both layers together in creating a smooth and uniform road surface.

This construction phase involves hauling in the rock, and then spreading and grading the rock over the road surface. It is highly recommended that this course of rock be rolled and compacted in place. An alternative strategy is to apply half (two inches or 5 cm) of the final crushed rock in one year or season and then apply a second and final running course of equal thickness later.

12. Trim trees and brush that shade the roadway.

Rock, asphalt, and concrete road surfaces all benefit from increased air circulation, drying heat, and better visibility that result from pruning adjacent roadway vegetation.

Pruning and removing unwanted vegetation results in improved lighting and enhances moisture evaporation. This is especially true with roads that are steep and possess multiple curves.

If the road is on a north or east-facing hillside that receives little or no sunlight, it is even more critical to keep the roadway dry and exposed to as much sunlight as possible. This action will enhance aesthetics, investment value, and safety.

Sounds Great But the Road Is Too Narrow. What Can We Do?

➤ Add road widening.

Widen the road. This may involve moving the ditchline, extending existing culverts, and building additional lateral distance. Or, it may entail cutting into a hillside to increase the roadway. It is surprising how much an additional two feet (61 cm) of width can improve a road.

➤ Add turnouts.

If your roadway is narrow or single-lane, consider adding a few wide spots along the road's edge that allow one vehicle to safely wait while another passes. These wide spots are called turnouts. See an example of one in Figure 3-4.

Properly located turnouts provide an alternative to riding in the ditches and backing up into driveways and side roads in order to allow traffic to pass. Keeping people out of the ditches is reason enough to

Figure 3-4. A turnout.

build smart turnouts. Once people lose respect for ditches, they drive in them causing the ditch to collapse, collect silt, and hold water. This leads to subgrade softening and ultimately, road failure.

When contemplating the addition of turnouts, you must first consider what the roadway will give. In other words, turnouts make sense where there's enough shoulder area to build one and where sight distance allows ample time for oncoming drivers to see and get out of each other's way. Ideal locations for turnouts include long stretches of roadway where vehicles can be seen over an extended distance, and at open expanses such as bridge and culvert crossing locations. They also work well at the narrowest sections of your roadway. Road constrictions caused by trees, rock outcroppings, and poles are prime candidates for turnout locations.

Turnouts require sufficient shoulder area on which to be built. Shoulders that exist on flat and gentle terrain work best for turnouts. Conversely, turnouts on steeper slopes and challenging grades present safety and traction issues. Construction costs increase with steeper ground, and the cost of building sufficient approaches in and out of such turnouts may prove prohibitive.

Construct turnouts wide enough to allow cars and pickups to safely pull aside and allow another vehicle to pass. And that is bare minimum.

They should also be long enough to allow large truck and trailer combinations to pull into. This includes logging trucks, dump truck and trailer combinations, school buses, fire trucks, and moving vans.

Turnouts can provide a key ingredient to solving roadway problems. They effectively increase your road's width without adding another continuous running lane. Once you have installed turnouts, be sure to install clearly marked signs instructing drivers to use them. This course of action better informs drivers who may be unfamiliar with your road and its alignment.

➤ Add pavement markings to concrete and asphalt.

Experienced drivers rely on visual boundaries such as roadway shoulders, painted lanes, and the alignment of opposing traffic. Without these references, drivers will gravitate toward the center of narrow and unmarked roadways thus creating an unsafe condition for oncoming traffic.

Hard surfaces also promote faster driving speeds, which further exacerbates conflicts with oncoming traffic. Once vehicles shift to avoid each other, the tires from either vehicle may steer off the pavement and damage the road's outer edge. Ditch, curb, and tire damage can also occur when vehicles leave the road surface.

On hard-surfaced roadways, you can help alleviate this condition by delineating driving lanes with paint or reflectors. This action is especially helpful on sharp curves where two-way traffic requires regulation type markers indicating lane delineation.

How Can a Turnout Work for Me if I Can't See Down the Road?

It can't. Part of any turnout plan involves removing any hill slopes, trees, and vegetation needed to improve sight distance and visibility. Additional grading and curve straightening may also be required to increase sight distance. There is no substitute for increased visibility when driving or trying to maintain vehicular safety.

✓ More "Do's"

- Do not cut corners.

- Always begin with the deepest work.

- Use the One-Call System before working.

- Give new roadwork a chance to settle out.

- Get rid of surface and below-ground water.

- Don't think twice about widening a road. Do it if you can.

- Investigate how using fabrics and grids can save you money.

- Find neighbors that will accept dirt and overexcavated material.

- Demand to do the job right when investing in permanent repairs.

- Dare to cut back vegetation more than your conscience allows.

- Understand that today's leaning trees are tomorrow's road-blocks.

- Build up your roadway by using step-by-step correct methodology.

- Delineate paved surfaces where lateral clearance or sight distance is lacking.

- Months before beginning work, search for cheap sources of structural material.

- Measure your culvert ends. They should extend at least two feet uncovered, beyond the roadway. Extend them if they are too short.

- Some engineers believe that a 10 percent thicker road will yield nearly 50 percent greater roadway fatigue life. Not a bad investment when considering the long-term financial, transportation, and social consequences attributable to roadway failure.

CHAPTER 4

The Mechanics of Restoring Hard Surfaced Roadways

How to Determine if Your Pavement is Failing

All pavements are inclined to fail. Slowly over time, cracks can develop, potholes will appear, and the running surface separates. The key to attaining maximum longevity begins with building quality road subgrade, providing ample shoulders, and paving properly. Sound roadways still need timely maintenance and care but when restoration is necessary, exercising proper repair techniques can extend the life of your road.

Recognizing the early stages of pavement failure and reacting to fix the problem is crucial to saving you time and money. In general, hard surface pavement fails due to one or more of the following problems:

1. Pavement abuse.

2. Excessive loading.

3. Poorly placed pavement.

4. Severe weather conditions.

5. Tree and vegetative intrusion.

6. Use of inferior paving products.

7. Poor or deficient pavement design.

8. Poor initial road base construction.

9. Changes in the ground conditions under paving.

10. Differential settling against dissimilar materials.

11. Inadequate shoulders and variations in elevation between road surface and shoulder.

➤ Signs of imminent or existing pavement failure include the following obvious indicators:

• Potholes.

Everyone's favorite! Potholes are holes developed within asphalt pavement and usually extend through to subgrade. Most potholes begin relatively small and most always develop due to weaknesses in subgrade (see Figures 4-1 and 4-2).

Figure 4-1. Potholed asphalt within a concrete transition zone.

Figure 4-2. Potholes in asphalt.

Asphalt potholes are harder on vehicles than unimproved dirt potholes because asphalt potholes develop sharp edges. These edges jolt vehicles when tires run into them. For drivers, asphalt edges make gauging the depth of potholes difficult since the hole's edge can hamper sight distance. A driver may not be able to tell where the bottom of the pothole is until they drive above or into it. By then, it's too late.

Concrete road sections develop potholes less often than asphalt because unlike asphalt, concrete doesn't readily tear, separate, and break down into random patterns. Broken and failed asphalt, if it doesn't crumble into a pot-hole, ends up being thrown to the road's edge. Meanwhile, finer asphalt particles slowly sink and become one with the earth much the same way a wounded ship slides beneath the waves, never to be seen again. It's not a pretty scenario for one's investment.

• Asphalt cracking and alligatoring.

Notice that Figures 4-3 and 4-4 show asphalt damage including cracks, squares, and geometric shapes. This pavement is suffering from fatigue usually caused by excessive loading, moisture, or subgrade failure.

Figure 4-3. Reflective cracking and alligatoring.

The weakened surface may last for a while and appear to have stabilized but fractured asphalt grows worse over time. Failed pavement degrades rapidly during cold and wet weather. When exposed to increased traffic and heavy trucking, damage accelerates.

When water infiltrates cracks and seams in broken pavement, the subgrade softens robbing the pavement of its firm structural support. If the water freezes and thaws, the pavement will heave and begin to break up. Pounding from vehicles further exacerbates the problem by pumping moist subgrade up and towards the road's surface resulting in broken pavement and potholing.

• Washboarding.

Ripples or corrugations that are transversely oriented to traffic flow indicate that the asphalt pavement is actually "rolling" under the tractive force of braking or pulling wheels. This happens when the asphalt is too

Figure 4-4. Potholes, cracking and heavy alligatoring.

thin or when it loses adhesion with the subbase. Washboarding is prevalent at the base of steep hills where traffic is braking down or accelerating up against the pavement.

• Roughness and irregularities.

Riding in a vehicle over such asphalt pavement is uncomfortable at best. Varying wheel loads and bouncing eventually fractures pavement resulting in potholes and alligatoring.

➤ Not-so-obvious signs of imminent or existing pavement failure include the following indicators:

• Longitudinal cracks in asphalt.

These cracks run parallel to traffic. As a result, they do not contrast well and may remain hidden from the eye. This type of failure can indicate that the subbase or fill beneath the roadway is fracturing and sliding away from the roadway itself. It can also indicate that traffic is weakening the subgrade parallel to vehicle flow because of concentrated loading along the travel lane.

- **Reflective cracking.**

Refer to Figure 4-3. Reflective cracking occurs when a newer top course of pavement begins to fail as a result of older pavement failing below it. This happens when:

1. New asphalt is laid upon an older course of weak and failed asphalt.
2. Pavement is laid upon failing concrete or above concrete joints.
3. Pavement is placed upon large boulders mixed into the subgrade.

Newer asphalt works to temporarily increase the pavement's resiliency thereby making this condition slower to spot. This problem is doubly

Figure 4-5. A supreme example of advanced asphalt segregation and cracks.

Figure 4-6. Cracked concrete driveway.

sneaky because most people aren't prone to seek signs of failure in freshly laid paving.

• Raveling and segregation.

What may be thought of as just another "look" for healthy asphalt is, in fact, a dangerous process where the asphalt product itself is disintegrating. In this situation, rock particles already in the mix begin to separate from the asphalt content within the pavement. This causes the asphalt to break away from itself, creating a depression and low spot.

As this depression attracts water, the affected area reacts to temperature differently than the balance of the roadway. Asphalt within the same road, moving at different rates, accentuates surface cracking and failure as portrayed in Figure 4-5. Water pockets are prone to subgrade saturation, ice formation and frost heave.

Depressions also collect and hold gravel and surface debris. They attract and accentuate the downward forces expelled by tires resulting in stressed subgrade and pavement failure.

Asphalt segregation can indicate poor construction, inferior asphalt, or inadequate design. As segregation occurs, the effective pavement thickness decreases lending itself to structural failure.

• Rutting.

Pavement ruts correspond with traffic wear and compressive downward stress. In more technical terms, rutting results from shear stress and subgrade deformation. Shallow channels form where tires repeatedly travel and develop into long, linear "birdbaths" that work to attract tires and hold water. Heavy loading, studded tires, poor subgrade, inadequate pavement thickness, a defective mix, and fast traveling vehicles can cause rutting. As a continuous depression, rutting leads to both longitudinal and transverse cracking that ends up in pavement failure. Rutting also lends itself to unsafe driving conditions in that it promotes hydroplaning and resists vehicle tracking.

• Concrete cracking.

Concrete failures almost always include some form of cracking. A cracked concrete driveway is shown in Figure 4-6. Cracks, whether in asphalt or concrete, let water infiltrate into the subgrade. As previously discussed, this promotes accelerated pavement damage and failure.

Concrete failures due to cracking differ from asphalt failures in a few ways. Being rigid, concrete tends to break into chunks, most of which are relatively large. Concrete chunks do not bend or break down below the road's surface. Instead, protruding edges and joint lines rise above the running surface creating great hazard and damage to vehicles, bicycles, and pedestrians.

Vegetative intrusion will also cause concrete to crack. These cracks are caused when tree and vegetative root systems burrow under concrete, causing the concrete section or panel to uplift until it cracks. Since concrete is weakest at the joint lines, the majority of cracking occurs there. However, mid-panel ragged breaks are not uncommon where concrete exists among trees, roots, and vegetation.

Unlike concrete, asphalt can flex over vegetative intrusion to a point, beyond which it also fails and requires repairs.

Inspecting Your Pavement

You can reasonably inspect your pavement by riding over it. What do you feel? How does the vehicle travel? What is the roadway telling you? Are your tires striking hard lips and edges indicating a raised and discontinuous paved surface? Does the asphalt roll and dip? Are there any depressions holding water along the road's surface? Does the roadway try to pull your vehicle to one side or another?

If you elect to walk the roadway to do a closer inspection, be sure to do it after a rain. Water can show a multitude of deficiencies in hard surfacing, such as puddles and rutting, and it shows best when wet. Even as a road surface initially dries, moisture in cracks and deep fissures will remain dark. Under these conditions, you will be able to clearly identify deterioration and the differences in shades make for ideal photography.

Spot Repairing Cracked and Broken Pavement

Worn-out and old sections of pavement can be removed and either recycled into usable products, or hauled to a dump. Loading, hauling, and dumping waste pavement can be quite costly. If possible, plan early to find locations for this material either within your project or close by in order to minimize dump costs later.

Replacing roadway pavement is expensive. The further you are from concrete and asphalt plants, the more you pay for hauling and placement. The following procedure is typical for replacing worn sections of asphalt and concrete.

➤ Identify where the pavement is failing.

Meet with a contractor or paving expert. Walk your roadway and get a professional opinion as to where the surfacing is weak and failing. Then decide with your neighbors exactly what you want to do. How much

Figure 4-7. Wholesale asphalt cut and removal.

pavement can you afford to replace. How much pavement do you need to replace? What is your time schedule?

Together as neighbors, walk the roadway and paint those areas slated for removal and replacement. Draw the failed areas on a plan carefully detailing areas of complete removal, areas of partial removal, and pothole repairs. Make copies of this plan for yourself, the contractor, and your neighbors. Measure the areas to be repaired in square feet (square meters) for record-keeping and cost-estimating purposes.

➤ A quick fix for limited potholes in asphalt.

Potholes in asphalt can be spot repaired or spray filled with products such as "permafill," "EZ Street," and "Patch-on-the-go." Cold asphalt repair materials such as these contain special polymers designed to ensure that the material adheres to the pothole, resists water penetration, remains flexible, and best of all, stays in the hole. Available in easy-to-handle sacks, you simply apply the patch material by placing the material in the hole and compacting it. Provided the subgrade has been fixed or remains a nonissue, the pothole should be fixed and immediately ready for traffic.

Figure 4-8. Paint marked, cut, and removed asphalt.

➤ Cut damaged areas slated for replacement.

Where roadway damage exceeds the size of potholes, large sections of failed pavement should be cut away from better and suitable surrounding pavement as exhibited in Figure 4-7. The shape and limit of such removals is determined by whatever area needs replacement. Unlike concrete, asphalt repair can be limited to the exact area needing restoration.

Begin by identifying the limits of damaged pavement and mark the affected areas with paint. Be sure to make the lines clean, clear, and straight. Once marked, the pavement is ready to be cut by use of a pavement-cutting saw. Most sawcutting is performed by subcontractors who specialize in such work, although, you may choose to cut smaller areas by hand. With sawcutting, simple geometric and right angle cut patterns work best.

When dealing with concrete, the contractor may choose to remove the damaged section or panel to the nearest joint. If the concrete has no joints, you now know that the absence of joints may be the primary culprit responsible for your concrete's failure! The reason is, joints give concrete room to move, expand, or shrink with temperature and moisture changes. They work to relieve stress within the concrete panel and help minimize cracking.

Because of joints and the occasional presence of steel reinforcement, concrete repairs tend to waste more good material than do asphalt repairs. Joints influence the limits of concrete replacement and repairs while providing a convenient and easy place from which to remove damaged roadway. In the end, concrete repaired within joint lines appears balanced and aesthetic.

With all damaged hardscape, actual cutting of the road surface is recommended. Figure 4-8 depicts surgically cut and removed asphalt. Cutting provides a clean and sharp edge to which new pavement can be matched. If the concrete has steel reinforcing, you will probably incur additional costs in cutting, loading and hauling away waste material.

Try to perform all possible project sawcutting at the same time including cutting any ragged edges and driveway cuts in preparation for matching future paving. When feasible, consolidate all sawcutting in order to reduce your cutting cost per lineal foot while limiting the cutting contractor's travel trips. If grading and paving result in raising the road's elevation, be sure to cut driveways and crossroads accordingly so that, when paved, they match your road with grace and properly drain water. Performing all sawcutting at once saves money since you'll only pay for one mobilization. The farther you are from civilization, the more it pays to be efficient.

If, after sawcutting driveways and crossroads, you decide not to pave them, place crushed rock neat to the fresh, cut edges so that they will be somewhat protected and ready when you later continue paving.

In some cases, thick sections of asphalt may be "butt ground" as a means of removal. Butt grinding is a process by which the limits of damaged asphalt are ground instead of cut. Grinding doesn't penetrate clear through the damaged asphalt but rather, carves out a tapered trough approximately two-inches (5 cm) deep into which, new asphalt is placed. See the section on cold planing.

➤ Remove all fractured and weak asphalt from cut areas.

Once the cuts have been completed, clean out the hole, load all worn sections and chunks of pavement and haul away. Removed pavement can be hauled off to a recycling center, used for chunk fill materials, or carted to your local dump. Since asphalt is petroleum based, special dump considerations may arise resulting in additional hauling costs. Ask your contractor or paver about this beforehand.

➤ Prepare the subgrade for fresh pavement.

Once the subgrade is exposed, the reasons for surface failures should be apparent. Soft areas of the subgrade must be excavated and replaced with pit-run or, preferably, crushed rock. Since water and sources of moisture must be removed or channeled away from underneath your roadway, your ability to add a continuous lift of free-draining material will help maintain moisture relief. (Refer to the subgrade-building portion of Chapter 3.)

It's also possible to partially bridge poor areas of subgrade with engineered fabric or grid. In some cases, it may be beneficial to just backfill the hole with concrete or crushed rock. If the holes are deep enough, it may make sense to dispose your broken asphalt and concrete chunks there but, be careful, as backfilling with random-sized material can be tricky. You must not only place and tamp chunk material deep enough and correctly, it should also be covered with an intermediary lift of suitable material and then capped with a grading course of $^3/_8$-inch or $^5/_8$-inch (10 mm or 16 mm) minus crushed rock

Use of broken roadway debris works best when the material chunks are small enough to work into place. The pieces must be small enough to allow you to compact under and around each chunk with no exceptions. You do not want nor can you afford air gaps and spaces when building subgrade. If your goal is to place all demolished pavement in the open subgrade, plan and budget for excavating and removing at least as much subgrade material out as you plan on "losing" or replacing back into the hole.

After filling and compacting the subgrade, lay a minimum of two inches (5 cm) of crushed rock or free-draining structural material over the surface in order to support and provide drainage under pavement.

➤ Pavement replacement.

Once the subgrade is repaired and a layer of free-draining material has been installed, the patch is now ready to accept either concrete or asphalt. If asphalt is chosen, all joints must be sealed after paving. Your paving contractor should supply and install this sealant once work is completed; however, be sure to request joint treatment anyway. Better to be safe than sorry.

➤ Pavement overlays and fabric.

Suitable existing pavement can be overlaid with additional asphalt. If the existing pavement is free of deformities and failed asphalt, paving fabrics can be added to ensure that new asphalt performs as expected—provided that the overlay is at least 1½-inches (4 cm) thick. Paving over insufficient older asphalt can result in many problems including reflective cracking.

Paving fabrics control subgrade water infiltration by adding a low-permeable membrane between pavement layers. This barrier keeps water from advancing upward into fresh pavement while providing a barrier to water migrating below it.

Fabrics can also provide structural support under pavements by adding tensile strength to the layers. This tensile strength combines with the natural compressive strength of asphalt and gravel to create a stiffer and stronger pavement. When paving over subgrade, fabrics work to enhance pavement performance by confining roadway aggregate. Consult with

Figure 4-9. The results of cold planing.

your paving contractor or supplier about the use of such fabrics for your particular paving situation.

Wholesale Repairs and Replacement of Failed Pavement

Mass failure of asphalt pavement does not necessarily mean it's a total loss. Options exist. To some degree, older material can be salvaged for many uses. In fact, depending on where your roadway is located, it may be possible to save up to 50 percent of the cost of new asphalt by recycling your roadway's existing asphalt.

➤ Here are a few alternatives available to help you deal with this problem.

• Cold planing.

If your asphalt is greater than two inches (5 cm) thick, and the surface fractures appear to be of hairline thickness or the surface is rough and suffering from pitting, then the top one or two (25 mm or 50 mm) inches may be "shaved" off and replaced with fresh asphalt. This shaving process is called cold planing.

Cold planing involves hiring a special piece of equipment or attachment that is capable of removing layers of old and damaged asphalt, the results of which are shown in Figure 4-9.

With cold planing, it is wise to begin at least one foot back (30 cm) into sound pavement, away from the area marked for removal. This ensures that you collect all fractured surface asphalt while improving your odds of success later in binding new asphalt onto older and firm pavement. After the selected thickness is planed off, a new asphalt cap is placed to grade within the planed area, creating the new road surface. As a result, any settling that occurs should be minimal and limited only to the new course of pavement.

The beauty of this system lies in the fact that new asphalt is placed into a monolithic, milled asphalt trough rather than filling a hole cut completely through the asphalt over raw subgrade. Of course, this approach works only if the subgrade and deeper paving are both firm and stable.

As opposed to cold planing, an asphalt patch that completely fills a "donut hole" cut through to raw subgrade must rely on the integrity of that subgrade to resist differential settling and subsequent failure. If the subgrade needs repairs, properly excavate and remove any wet and organic materials, add a structural rock base and prepare it to receive asphalt.

• Complete grinding.

If your paved roadway is failing in mass proportion with heaving, multiple cracking, or deep potholing, a complete repaving project may be your only option.

Complete grinding is a method of removing all affected asphalt and grinding it into a reusable road base product. In this case, old and broken asphalt is completely ground into a finer rock product that can be re-used as part of a supporting base course for new asphalt.

The process begins by employing an asphalt-grinding machine to pulverize the entire roadway. If the subgrade needs to be reworked, the volume of ground asphalt removed should be temporarily stockpiled away from the construction zone. This reconstituted material can be added to new structural dirt or imported rock, or it can be laid over the road subgrade and roller compacted into place. The result in using this material is that you will either need less rock when building your sub-base up or you will have a stronger subgrade upon which your subbase rock may be placed. At least you'll save in not having to have to pay to haul it off.

Ground asphalt is an excellent roadway component suitable for long-term roadway stability. Once this material is ground in place, it can be graded and compacted into a structural subbase course, ready to accept fresh asphalt.

Complete grinding offers many other benefits including reusing a product that would otherwise be expensive to load, haul, and dump. Dump rates can be extremely high for waste asphalt. Another benefit is the added structural component that ground and compacted asphalt adds to a roadbed. This bonus layer of material helps to lengthen road life and can help reduce the thickness of your new pavement section. In the end, it feels good to recycle and it feels good to do things smartly, but it really feels good knowing that you're also saving money at the same time.

Ground asphalt is a flexible construction product. It can be used for walking paths, trails, and light duty driveways. Applications for this recon-stituted material are endless. The only restriction on its use is having the right weather during which to lay it down and the ultimate quantity of material that you end up salvaging. The warmer the weather, the easier it will be to grade and form reconstituted asphalt, but as a rule, this holds true for all asphalt products and paving activity.

• Cold, in-place pavement reconstruction.

This alternative is similar to grinding with one major difference: the older asphalt, ground in place, is mixed with a cold, emulsified binding agent and relaid as *new pavement*. This happens without ever removing the ground material from the roadway. Landowners who want to save money or who live a considerable distance away from a hot mix asphalt plant may find this alternative appealing.

The drawbacks of this process include the following:

1. Keeping the reconstituted asphalt clean and uniform. As a subgrade constituent, reconstituted asphalt complements rock and improves structural dirt. However, if the ground asphalt is too thin or is inadvertently mixed with foreign material such as organic soil, fine-grained material, and woody debris, the mix may not bind sufficiently in spite of added emulsion. The resulting pavement may be prone to failure and is liable to quickly fracture and delaminate along zones of contamination.

2. Having enough ground asphalt to work with. If the original ground asphalt quantity is not sufficient, this process will not work as fully as intended. You may need to add fresh emulsion, crushed rock, or more clean ground asphalt product in order to make up the difference. Lack of sufficient ground material may also force you into purchasing hot mix in order to complete the job.

3. Increased air voids. What does increased air voids mean? It means that you have more air gaps and space between and within roadway materials than you should have. In more technical terms, your roadway is lacking the consolidation and compaction required for long-term performance. This equates to an increased probability of premature roadway failure because of water infiltration and freezing, gradual settling over time, and potholing.

Cold, in-place reconstituted pavement tends to have more air voids and cavities when relaid as road surfacing than does hot mix asphalt. This is because existing cold material is just that, it is cold and stiff. Without reheating, cold mix asphalt needs significant rolling and compaction to attain any shape or hope for consolidation.

Temperature is very important. Cold mix, in-place reconstituted pavement should be placed during warm weather conditions. Being black, the mix will absorb sunlight and gain a measure of surface flexibility. By working to eliminate air voids, you not only minimize the likelihood of settling and surface indentation, you greatly improve your chances of enjoying stable and smooth pavement. Of course, temperature is only one variable that you need to account for.

Another is adequate resistance for rolling. Successful compaction of pavement can only happen when the material is rolled against an immovable and firm surface. There's no other way. Thus, it's imperative that cold-mix material be laid over an unyielding and stable subgrade. Unsuitable subgrades involve rebuilding, and marginal subgrades still may need rock and compaction in order to be hard enough to pave against.

4. This alternative is not a panacea for poor subgrade. Cold *(or hot)* reconstituted asphalt pavement will not "fix" all problems that arise due to poor subgrade. If the asphalt is failing due to weakened or nonexistent subgrade, the surface pavement must be removed and the subgrade improved. Otherwise, the new product will fail in similar fashion as the older pavement failed. Reconstituted cold material has been known to quickly pothole; a condition that you can rectify with fresh asphalt resurfacing.

5. Weather. Any phase of sitework is weather dependent. Ground asphalt exposed to increased moisture and near freezing temperatures is no different. It will not mix, grade, or compact if conditions aren't just right.

• **Chip seal.**

Consider chip sealing paved roads that are in need of a new asphalt overlay. Chip sealing, also known to some as macadam, is a process of paving by which the road surface is first covered with a binder of either cement or asphalt liquid emulsion (tar), and then overlaid with a lift of crushed gravel or rock. The mixture is then compacted. Chip seal is considered a surface treatment only and is not meant to replace wholesale paving as a long-term, hard surface solution.

For maximum life expectancy, chip sealing must be performed under dry and warm conditions. The existing roadway should be first cleaned and repaired of any potholes and alligatoring. Once the emulsion is sprayed, clean aggregate should immediately be placed and rolled into it in order to minimize loss of gravel and promote maximize adhesion. Incorrectly sized gravel aggregate or too much emulsion can result in bleeding and weakened chip seal. On the other hand, carefully monitor contractors that place too much gravel knowing that adequate coverage will be attained at the expense of wasting inordinate amounts of excess rock. Chip seal offers the following benefits:

- Skid resistance.
- Relative low cost.
- Highly water resistant.
- It goes down quickly as several miles of chip seal can be applied in a day.
- As a hot binder, it finds, fills, and covers surface cracks and shallow dips.
- Chip seal is best suited for roads that receive low to medium traffic volumes.
- Depending on the condition of your roadway, chip seal may last a decade before needing to be reapplied.

Options for Dealing with Cracked and Broken Concrete

Worn out concrete that doesn't contain steel reinforcement can usually be broken into usable chunk material by use of ordinary construction machinery. Otherwise, depending upon the size of broken material that you're interested in, "rubbleizing" by use of a high-frequency hammer or dropping dead weight from heights are two methods commonly used to crack and seat worn concrete.

Paved Roadway Alternatives

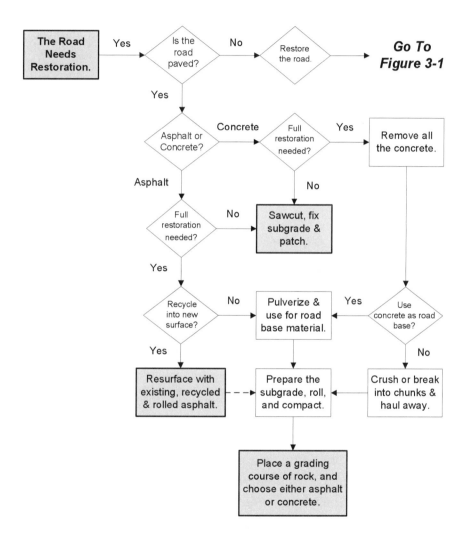

Figure 4-10.

Succeeding with older broken concrete as a roadway additive depends on the quality of the cement and rock used in the original mix. Rotten concrete or very old and unstructural cement may continue to break down if added into a new roadway or if interfaced with harder crushed rock. You or your contractor should spend some time evaluating any old concrete before you decide how and where to reuse it. Unfortunately, concrete tends to break into chunks too large for shallow road fills or for use in minor repair work.

Another detriment of broken concrete is that it cannot be easily re-constituted with an emulsion or liquid binder in order to create road surfacing.

Breaking unreinforced concrete into a *smaller,* gravel-sized, and gradable product is expensive and usually not practical for small road jobs. In fact, cost saving ideas that rely on crushing and process recycling work best on larger scale projects where it's worth paying the fixed cost to set up a recycling operation. Evaluate the cost of trucking, materials, and the distance to the nearest material source *against* the cost to handle, crush, and store recycled products. Also evaluate the land area needed for equipment, stockpiling, and operations. Savings, if they exist, should be apparent. In both cases, material handling and grading costs will be comparable.

Where crushing and processing old concrete makes sense, an even mix of finely crushed concrete can be produced by employing an in-place crushing machine that collects larger concrete chunks, grinds them in-place, adds water if necessary, and lays the new material onto the roadway via a beltway or by loader.

Most landowners will find it more economical to forego crushing concrete and just break it up into larger chunks. In this form, the material can still be used as chunk material for improving subbase, adding turnouts, and for use in road widening.

Another alternative for larger (greater than 12-inch or 30 cm) crushed concrete material is to use it in building short, (less than 3-foot or 90 cm high) hand-placed retaining walls. The material is cheap and when constructed properly, looks terrific.

Preparing Roadways for Pavement

Any properly constructed road subgrade can accept asphalt or concrete. The beauty in constructing your roadway properly is that you now have a sound investment *and* you have alternatives. Depending on your budget and timetable, alternatives include keeping your roadway in an unimproved crushed rock condition or moving forward with hard-paved surfacing.

Hard surfacing can be achieved by either placing concrete or paving with asphalt. Refer to Figure 4-10, the pavement alternative decision tree. Although hard surfacing may be considered a luxury by rural standards, there is no substitute for a properly constructed roadway that can support it. If concrete or asphalt is desired, it may not be necessary to apply the final running course of crushed rock as previously discussed. At least, it may not have to be as thick.

When considering hardscape, you may only need enough crushed rock topping to allow for fine grading in preparation for paving. A layer, two inches (5 cm) thick of $^3/_8$-inch or $^5/_8$-inch (10 mm or 16 mm) minus crushed rock may do the trick. The paving contractor, civil engineer, or a qualified construction consultant could help you to decide.

Here's another tip. Kill any weeds before paving or placing hard surfacing. Weeds will find any and all cracks and joints and may also grow under asphalt pavement when exposed to the sun's radiant heat. If you have significant weeds growing where you want to pave, it's best to kill them by spraying and then hold off until late summer or fall to pave. This time period is ideal since all weeds should have germinated and seasonal dryness still promises good construction weather.

➤ Should we pave directly on native subgrade?

The answer depends upon many factors including the following:

1. Your budget.
2. Native soil type.
3. The ability to adhere.

4. Your geographic location.

5. Existing subgrade density.

6. Degree of native soil moisture.

7. Roadway firmness, shape, and grade.

8. Thickness of proposed road surfacing.

9. The ability of your subgrade to drain and pass water.

For longevity, hard surfacing needs drainage and support. It also needs to adhere to something. If your native soils are coarse-grained, that is, they contain a significant proportional amount of sand, gravel, and cobbles, it *may* be possible to successfully place hard surfacing directly without penalty. Of course, you may have to contend with the other eight factors mentioned above before agreeing to surface directly on coarse-grained native soils.

The above eight factors become even *more* critical when one considers surfacing directly on native fine-grained soils such as silts and clay. Fine-grained soils tend to comprise higher moisture levels, questionable strength, and an inability to absorb water intrusion. None of these characteristics bode well for hard surface longevity.

In either case, provided the native subgrade is suitable and properly prepared, a layer at least two inches thick of $^3/_8$-inch or $^5/_8$-inch (10 mm or 16 mm) minus crushed rock may suffice prior to paving. However, to be safe, you need to be sure that your native subgrade *is* suitable for surfacing. Take the advice of a geotechnical consultant or a civil engineer before deciding that your native subgrade is ready for hard surfacing. Otherwise, you may be gambling. If budget constraints dictate paving directly on native soils and you proceed without professional counsel, you may be at risk for partial or wholesale road failure.

If you have placed years upon years of rock into your road subgrade, the rock quantity may have built-up enough to somewhat stabilize the road surface. In this case, a thin section of two inches of crushed rock may be enough to provide drainage and a grading course in preparation for surfacing, but, again, if you have the resources to pave or place concrete, it costs little more to seek professional guidance. It's analogous to that old "penny-wise, pound-foolish" saying that's so familiar and true.

Deciding between Asphalt and Concrete

The many intrinsic benefits of hard surfacing are evident. Long-term investment and reduced maintenance are primary reasons to surface unimproved gravel roadways. Bearing in mind that the following discussion, comparisons, and comments only pertain to commonly found mixes and everyday, off-the-shelf stock products, choosing between properly laid asphalt and properly placed concrete as roadway surfacing should depend on many factors including the following:

➤ Characteristics and advantages of asphalt.

- Asphalt is seamless.
- Asphalt is smoother and results in quieter traffic.
- Asphalt goes down quickly and can accept traffic sooner.
- Asphalt doesn't accept reinforcing steel or fiber in the mix.
- The dark color of asphalt absorbs heat, quickly melting snow and ice.
- There is minimal material waste with asphalt and no trucks to clean onsite.
- Asphalt is usually cheaper depending upon project location. Net savings resulting from using asphalt depends upon the amount of alternative concrete forming that would be required, and by comparing the ultimate thicknesses of both products. However, it is important to remember that the cost of asphalt is in part, tied to price fluctuations and availability within the oil and petroleum industry.
- Asphalt paving sections tend to be thinner than concrete

sections. With adequate road base and drain rock, 2 inches (5 cm) of asphalt is usually enough. This results in less exposed edge, less excavation and grading, and easier grade transitions and matching to adjoining driveways.

- Asphalt overlays are usually thinner than concrete "white topped" overlays. Concrete white-topped overlays performed over stable and firm asphalt result in very stout road sections. As a road restoration treatment, white-topping is expensive and usually not considered by private landowners.

- Asphalt flexes with subgrade movement. It flexes in the heat of sunlight and warm weather. It will also shrink with weather.

- As a product to itself, asphalt will not quickly crack and degrade from water and ice. However, it may allow a degree of water infiltration unless a moisture barrier (paving fabric) is integrated into the design. Hot mix asphalt combined with rolling and compacting can act to draw water up into the subgrade while laying down pavement.

- Before settling upon a final graded road profile such as "crowned" versus "uniform sloped", research your options as to which sized paving machines are available and at what cost. Smaller machines, although fine for narrow driveways and paths may not be adequate for paving wide, continuous, and uniformly graded roads. Likewise, larger highway sized machines may not work on narrow or center crowned roadways. Consult with a paving contractor before committing to your road's final graded profile.

➤ Characteristics and advantages of concrete.

- Concrete reflects light and heat.
- Concrete can be mixed to a custom color.

- Temperature does not affect concrete as much as asphalt.
- Concrete can accept a decorative pattern and traction scoring.
- Traffic will not break the roadway edges of concrete as readily as it will asphalt.
- Concrete is not as sensitive as asphalt to deterioration from gasoline and other solvents.
- Concrete can be reinforced with steel or synthetic fibers for added strength and stiffness.
- Being more brittle than asphalt, concrete can crack due to fluctuations in temperature and heavy loading.
- Concrete provides better traction and may shed water better than asphalt depending upon final finish.
- Concrete sections are usually four- to seven-inches (10 cm to 18 cm) thick, resulting in a higher road profile than comparable asphalt.
- Unless an expensive slip-paving machine is used, concrete roads will need to be formed by hand and stripped after the concrete hardens. Concrete placed by hand usually results in a rougher surface than machine-placed concrete.
- Concrete can "bridge" minor subgrade settling. Although this may be a positive attribute, the amount of "bridging" that concrete can perform before failing is limited, depending on the strength and thickness of the concrete mix as well as the amount of steel reinforcing used.

➤ Disadvantages of hard road surfacing (both asphalt and concrete).

- High cost to establish and repair.
- Susceptibility to freezing and holding cold.
- When wet, reflects glare from street lighting and vehicle headlights.

- Potential need for planning, engineering, surveying, and design services.

- Hard surfaces cause water and runoff to concentrate in higher volumes and move quicker.

- Faster vehicle speeds. Traffic speeds tend to increase with paving resulting in the additional cost and inconvenience of adding speed deterrents such as bumps and signage.

- Susceptibility to damage due to ignorant actions. Hard surfaces aren't invincible and abuses such as running track equipment down a surfaced roadway will help to quickly destroy your investment. This problem becomes magnified with neighbors who abstain from paying for such investments and as a result, either don't think clearly about damaging it, or have no reason to treat the road with respect.

- Protruding ridges or lips where elevations differ. If an equal thickness of material is not removed to compensate for placing new surfacing, the road will rise above its former elevation. Likewise, adjoining driveways and crossroads must receive the same treatment or get "feathered" into the new road in order to keep all surfaces even. Roadway shoulders may also have to be raised or re-graded in order to match the road's new elevation. Matching shoulder grade to the road's new elevation protects the edge of surfacing, protects tires, better ensures safety, and is aesthetic. (See Chapter 7, problems with dissimilar materials.)

➤ Complications related to hard surface construction.

- The further your project is from processing plants, the more expensive and riskier it is to haul moisture- and temperature-sensitive materials such as asphalt and concrete. Loss of temperature in asphalt, or concrete being too hot or cold, can result in either product being unworkable once delivered and upon setting-up, prone to premature failure.

- If the concrete supplier (contractor) begins adding too much water to compensate for moisture loss or for cooling down the concrete mix due to extended trucking distance, the strength and consistency of the mix may be compromised. This can result in a weaker product that is harder to manipulate and one that sets up poorly.

- In as much as long travel time causes concrete to heat up, increased haul distance over 35 or so miles (56 km) causes hot mix asphalt to do the opposite, it cools down. Cool asphalt does not lay and bind as well as hot mix will. As asphalt cools, it drifts away from what is called, its "*tender*" period. The tender period is that time when asphalt is at the optimal temperature and consistency required for proper placement.

- Hauling hot mix asphalt over long trucking distances or over rough roadways can cause the mix to overvibrate, leading to product segregation. Segregation means that some of the crushed rock aggregate in the asphalt has separated from the liquid emulsion. Usually, the larger crushed rock aggregate dislodges from the emulsion and, in doing so, rolls to the corners of the truck bed. Meanwhile, the finer rock aggregate stays in the middle of the box. A mix such as this can result in an inconsistent and stiff delivery. Asphalt roads built with segregated mix are rough, porous, and uneven.

- In-place segregation is manifested when you can clearly see the entire outline of rocks in the final paved product. The asphalt appears coarse and the rock looks like it can be easily picked out with a hand-tool. The larger the rock used in the mix, the easier it is to spot segregation.

- More expensive and finer mixes may not appear to exhibit

segregation immediately after being laid. Instead, if these mixes eventually segregate, it will show within a year or so after the road has been paved.

- On one hand, too much emulsion leaves pavement weak. On the other, too much rock without emulsion doesn't bind together resulting in raveling and an uneven surface. In the long run, strength and resiliency to weather will suffer if asphalt mix is laid when cold.

- The next time you travel over a remote paved area, note the poor surface quality and material segregation within the running surface. It's to be expected when the mix cools and separates over long travel distances.

- Asphalt that loses its tender condition may be enhanced with additional compaction or by agitating the mix before laying it, however, this results in higher costs and doesn't always produce results as expected.

✓ **More "Do's"**

- Understand how concrete and asphalt vary.

- Install hard surfacing to improve water quality.

- Read the condition of your pavement after a good rain.

- Locate a place suitable to waste excess concrete or asphalt.

- With your engineer, explore life cycle costing for each material.

- Understand that once you lay hard surfacing, you're committed.

- Cost compare asphalt versus concrete relative to your project location.

- Make sure that all below-grade utilities and pipes are in before paving.

- Look for constructive ways to use chunk and ground asphalt or concrete.

- Understand that hard surfacing is only as good as, and will reflect the subgrade it sits upon.

- Plan to place hard surfacing during the warmest and driest time of the year.

- Understand that longer haul distances work against attaining quality paving.

- Consult with your contractor and supplier before making any final decisions.

- Leave yourself lots of time to plan for and schedule hard surface construction.

- Import and fine grade enough small-sized crushed rock when preparing to pave.

- Be prepared for the changes and issues that accompany newly surfaced roadways.

- Eliminate surrounding road area problems that bear upon and create pavement failure.

- Prepare for increased water drainage volumes and velocity after applying hard surfacing.

- Following paving, while the base rock is still loose and dry, rake it out along the shoulder.

- Learn how fabrics, grid, and fiber reinforcement can save you money and effectively strengthen your surfacing.

- Before committing to a supplier, inspect the appearance, quality, and durability of their materials as placed on projects comparable to yours.

- If you are planning to pave a road that is significantly distant from the nearest asphalt plant, try to locate a paving contractor that employs remixer type, auger machinery. Such paving equipment works to remix asphalt before placing it thereby reducing segregation.

CHAPTER 5

Some Other Things You Should Know

Optimal Conditions for Performing Road Restoration or New Construction

➤ Seasonal issues.

From a cost standpoint, the ideal time to perform construction is when contractors charge less. That time occurs during their seasonally slow periods. The problem is, *sitework* contractors experience slow periods when it makes sense to slow-down. They usually go dormant when demand lessens, during holidays, and when seasonally poor weather drives them inside.

Since road construction is extremely weather sensitive, capitalizing on your contractor's slack period may prove to be your *most expensive* alternative. Autumn and spring offer the best potential combination of lower contractor pricing and lower material costs depending, of course, on weather. If you get lucky and it's dry, you save money. If it pours rain during construction, you'll pay plenty in extra costs.

Summer is the most expensive time to perform sitework because contractors are busy and demand soars for their services. Contractors also like summer work because it brings dependable weather and longer daylight hours. This equates into larger and more profitable projects. Winter is the least attractive time to perform earthwork or paving due to increased moisture, lower temperatures, and shorter days. Plus, nobody is really motivated to work during the holidays.

Other factors that affect the right time to perform work can include company size, current workload, and the contractor's overall capability. Some contractors can't resist the opportunity to work a privately funded project instead of going after public works jobs. Still, many other issues play into contracting roadwork at the optimal time, so you have to ask yourself a question. What is more important to you? Cost of construction or construction schedule? If your road needs restoration or you plan on selling your home soon, no time is better than the present to fix your roadway.

➤ Regulatory issues.

Another reason to act quickly is to avoid being stymied by zoning and land-use changes. There exists a growing perception that "urban sprawl" and rural migration should be slowed or even halted. This way of thinking works to tighten zoning and increase regulation. Those who wish to develop their property may find their right to access challenged or even denied due to unknown or lurking land controls. Environmental restrictions can severely limit use of your land. In similar fashion to water rights or septic approval requirements, they can prohibit you from ever using your land the way that you had intended. These types of hindrances work against owning property as a long-term investment and certainly raise yet another land issue—private property rights.

In the big picture, it's wise to *act now* if you are planning to restore your roadway. Work to establish access and plan new construction into or across your property while striving to reach that "sweet spot" where lower contractor cost and reasonable weather work to your advantage. Be mindful of zoning issues that will or may affect your land and neighborhood. It's also wise to act quickly before creeping construction standards and lengthening permit processes cost you more money. Roadwork promises two things that you *can count on.* Things usually get more complicated and they become increasingly expensive if left over time.

Treasures Commonly Discovered During Road Work
Not To Scale

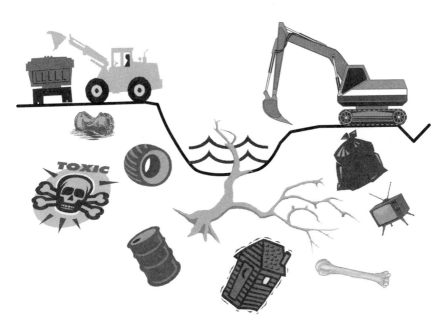

Figure 5-1. Possibilities awaiting your discovery.

Surprises and Unknowns When Dealing in Road Work

The possibilities for unearthing hidden goodies (See Figure 5-1) during roadwork are endless. Here's a list of common surprises that you may encounter when excavating into the bowels of your road:

- Trees.
- Water.
- Car bodies.
- Abandoned utility lines.

- Artifacts from an old dump.

- Existing and live utility lines.

- Rocks, boulders, and bedrock.

- Stumps, limbs, and woody debris.

- Crushed culverts and broken pipes.

- Boards and debris from old buildings.

- Swampy and supersaturated wetland soils.

- Logs and wooden beams used as "corduroy" (a method of installing ties perpendicular to the road alignment) in supporting a road.

- Bones? Did someone find bones?

Construction Equipment Required for Restoration and Repair Work

Choosing road construction equipment depends upon three things:

1. The task.

2. Your location.

3. Your budget.

Depending upon the task or phase of construction, the following equipment is designed to handle repairs, restoration, and new road construction:

➤ Culvert and pipe installation.

- An excavator or backhoe for digging, lifting the culvert sections into place, and for backfilling.

- An excavator or backhoe with a mechanical tamp or a hand-operated compactor for soil compaction.

- Possible use of a front-end loader or bulldozer for excavation and backfill purposes.

- Possible trucking and material delivery.

➤ Pothole excavation and repairs.

- An excavator or backhoe for digging out rotten pothole material and replacing it with rock or structural material.

- A front-end loader that delivers backfill to the work zone from a stockpile area.

- An excavator or backhoe with a mechanical tamp or a hand-operated compactor for soil compaction. In places where the roadway receives minimal use or light traffic, with the right soils and weather, it may be possible to compact pipe backfill by walking heavy, rubber-tired equipment over successive layers of backfill. These layers or courses of backfill are commonly called "lifts."

- Possible trucking and material delivery.

➤ Cut to fill, grade improvements, curve straightening, road widening, and rough grading.

- An excavator, backhoe, or track bulldozer with either a blade or front-end bucket attachment.

- A road grader for surface blading, creating drainage trenches, and ditch cleaning.

- A static drum compactor for soil compaction.

- Possible trucking and material delivery.

➤ Roadway fine grading.

- A road grader or bulldozer with a straight blade.

- A static drum compactor for soil compaction.

➤ Spreading or grading roadway rock.

- A road grader or bulldozer with either a straight blade or front-end bucket attachment. Some contractors prefer an excavator or rubber-tired backhoe for spreading rock.
- A static drum compactor for rock compaction.
- Trucking and rock delivery.

➤ Final surface preparation.

- A static nonvibrating drum compactor.
- If the roadway is slightly uneven or cut edges remain exposed, a small bulldozer or road grader may also be required for final blading.

➤ Placement of asphalt or concrete.

- Sawcut machine.
- Material delivery trucks.
- A screed or paving machine.
- Possibly a cold planing or pulverizing machine.
- An excavator or backhoe for loading out chunk material.
- A road grader or small bulldozer for spot grading.
- A concrete pumper may be required for concrete construction or paving.
- A static drum compactor for asphalt and possibly also for concrete will be required if the road is designed for roller-compacted concrete. (The latter is extremely unlikely, as this type of concrete construction is expensive and usually performed only in heavy, industrial, and public works applications.)

Materials and Supplies Required for Restoration and Repair Work

Materials vary according to the extent of construction, soil conditions, and your geographic area. You may need any combination of the following materials to fix your road:

➤ Most likely items.

- Grass seed.
- Geotextile fabric or grid.
- Drain rock and rounded gravel.
- Delivered select fill dirt or pit-run.
- Purchase or rental of detour traffic signage.
- Delivered crushed rock of varying sizes and gradations.
- Culvert or piping for conveying water or utility lines under roadways or driveways.

➤ Possible items.

- Retaining wall components.
- Dewatering pump and hoses.
- Erosion control fencing and stakes.
- Reconstituted and chunk concrete or asphalt material.

Choosing Culvert and Pipe Material

Choice of culvert and pipe material depends upon diameter, burial depth, weight per section, availability, and, ultimately, cost. Unless an engineer has specified a pipe size and material or your contractor has offered such, there are many pipe materials to choose from. If you are doing the job yourself, ease of installation should be a priority when selecting type of culvert pipe.

Installing culvert and pipe is an art. Culverts must support the roadway, channel water, and remain, at worst, level. Culvert installation can involve a great degree of hand shoveling and survey control. If you are installing culverts yourself, seek advice; ask lots of questions, and start very early in the day. Also be prepared. Many pipe suppliers are not open on weekends and holidays.

With the exception of concrete, most pipe comes in standard 20-foot (6 meters) lengths or rolls. Unless you have an extended flatbed truck and like hoisting pipe around, it is recommended that all pipe material be purchased as delivered to your jobsite. If you have the trench ready before accepting pipe delivery, you may be able to have the delivery truck lay the pipe sections as you want them so that you can easily connect and backfill them.

Buried culverts can be round, oval, half-round, and rectangular. In situations where headroom is lacking or loading is great enough to require design and engineering, you may need to install pipe other than round. If so, leave installation to a professional contractor.

Here are some tips to consider when selecting culvert and pipe:

➤ Plastic pipe.

Plastic pipe is a cheap and logical alternative when your application requires smaller diameter pipe. Best of all, it is relatively easy to handle and install. In most cases, plastic culvert can be installed without the use of heavy equipment. It is easy to cut and repair and will last indefinitely. Most flexible plastic pipe is black in color and can be integrated into landscape designs.

Plastic pipe comes in two forms; rigid and flexible. Both types of pipe can usually be purchased locally in lumberyards, hardware stores, and specialty outlets.

• Rigid plastic pipe.

Rigid plastic pipe joints can be connected by using liquid primer and glue in similar fashion to assembling a PVC lawn irrigation system. This type of pipe can be cut by hand sawing or by use of a power saw. Rigid pipe is available in a multitude of thickness and 24-inch (600 mm) and less diameter pipe can be easily manipulated by hand. Rigid plastic pipe tends to increase dramatically in cost with thickness and as diameters approach and exceed 30 inches (750 mm). Heavy-gauge, rigid plastic pipe is usually recommended for sanitary sewer purposes.

- **Flexible plastic pipe.**

Flexible plastic pipe can also be purchased in a multitude of sizes and thicknesses. It's lighter in weight when compared to most other culvert alternatives of the same diameter and assembles very easily with snap-type mechanical fittings. Flexible pipe has a firm corrugated exterior but the inside is smooth thus allowing water and debris to freely flow through. It's an attractive culvert alternative for the "do-it-your-selfer."

Be forewarned though when installing flexible pipe. It's very sensitive and unforgiving if not compacted properly or if it's not laid appropriately. Being flexible in nature, this type of pipe cannot accommodate "bridging" or any lack of support. Shoddy installation manifests itself in pipe deflection, settling, and lateral failure.

Headroom distance is also more critical with flexible pipe. Headroom distance is the distance between the top of pipe and roadway running surface. In general, depending upon pipe diameter, thickness, and manufacturer, the absolute safe *minimum* headroom for flexible pipe is approximately 18 inches (46 cm) provided that it's properly compacted and backfilled with suitable structural material. Check and adhere to the manufacturer's specifications to be sure.

Flexible plastic pipe is highly resistant to freeze/thaw cycles and corrosive conditions but it's not suitable for sanitary sewer purposes. With all nonconducible pipe, install a "tracer wire" so that you can locate the pipe later after it has been buried.

Figure 5-2. Galvanized steel culvert damage.

➤ Steel pipe.

Steel pipe has been used for culverts for many years. Installed correctly, steel products can last a long time and provide adequate water passage. Under similar conditions, aluminum pipe lasts even longer than steel.

• Galvanized steel and aluminum culverts.

Galvanized steel and aluminum culverts are relatively light and connect with collars and bolts. Their walls are thin and damage easily (See figure 5-2) but they can be readily cut with a power saw. Although more expensive, aluminum culvert will resist corrosion and is lighter than galvanized steel pipe of equal diameter. Steel pipe is readily available during the week, however it may be tough to obtain on weekends when most commercial suppliers are closed.

Aluminum pipe may be slightly more difficult to get without giving prior notice to suppliers. Smaller diameter galvanized steel and aluminum culverts can be installed by hand without use of heavy equipment.

Figure 5-3. Ductile iron culvert manifold.

• Heavy-duty steel alternatives.

Heavy-duty steel alternatives are available for large diameter pipes and where extremely heavy roadway loadings are expected. For the most part, heavy commercial piping products are "bullet proof."

These pipe alternatives include ductile iron and plate steel. Multiple small diameter ductile iron pipes can be grouped together for handling increased volumes of water as illustrated in Figure 5-3. If you are installing this type of pipe, you'll also be hiring a professional with equipment and experience adequate enough to do the job. Ductile iron, concrete, and steel pipe are heavy. Without heavy lifting equipment, tight trench control, and proper fittings (no, duct tape won't work), your task could become a royal nightmare.

One option worth mentioning is contacting your local water district or utility contractors to see if they will be removing any ductile iron waterlines sometime in the future. Used ductile iron waterline pipe that is unacceptable for reuse in potable water systems works great as culvert. It's especially useful where you have no option but to install a shallow culvert with minimal dirt or crushed rock fill directly above it. Ductile iron pipe is strong and will survive both trucks and the pounding of fast-moving cars. To a large degree, it can withstand substandard compaction and poor backfilling practices. I've supported fully loaded, off-road trucks and scrapers with only a foot of headroom over used ductile iron water-line pipe. It's dependable, cost effective, and recycled.

➤ Concrete pipe.

Concrete pipe is usually manufactured and delivered in eight-foot (240 cm) lengths. It's very heavy in *any diameter* and connects by placing the "spigot" or straight end of the pipe into the "bell" section of the pipe.

It is crucial that the bell end of each pipe section be placed forward, or upgrade of flow, so that the potential for leakage is minimized.

Where extreme vehicle loading or excessive vertical downward shock is expected, this type of pipe can be ordered with varying degrees of steel reinforcement. Only experienced pipe utility contractors should install concrete pipe due to its weight, clumsiness, and shorter lengths.

Pipe length is a critical element in determining ease of installation. The shorter the pipe sections, the more pieces there are to join. Multiple, short pieces of pipe are tough to install without continual survey control and qualified manpower.

For most road associations and private landowners, concrete pipe may not be a viable alternative since it's application is specific to heavy load-ings and can be quite expensive to install.

➤ The wooden box culvert.

For years, wooden box culverts have been used as a cheap and effec-tive tool for moving water across dirt and gravel roadways. Being three-sided with an open top, box culverts also act as a "trench drain" in that they are able to intercept and collect road surface runoff.

Box culverts are easily constructed, relatively cheap, and quick to in-stall. See Figure 5-4 for box culvert details or Figure 5-5 for the same de-tails expressed in metric terms. Box culvert maintenance is a snap and

The Open Top Wooden Box Culvert
Not To Scale

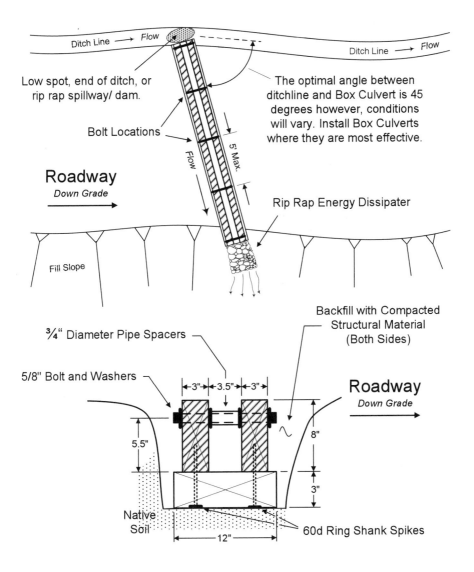

Figure 5-4. Wooden box culvert.

The Open Top Wooden Box Culvert
Not To Scale (Metric Version)

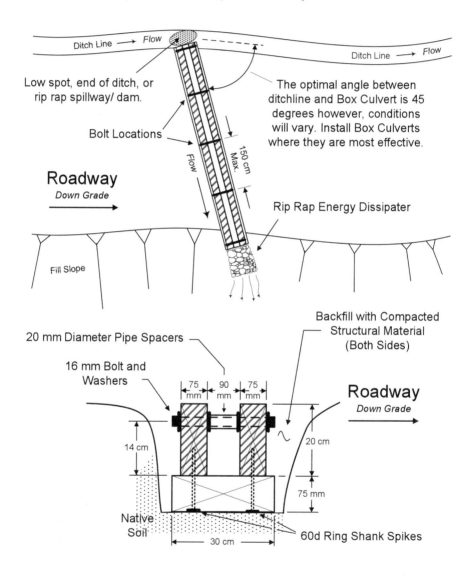

Figure 5-5. Wooden box culvert.

culvert replacement can be accomplished without requiring heavy equipment. In some cases, where mild topography prohibits use of below ground pipes to adequately pass low volumes of ditch water or where it is preferable to install shallow pipes due to bedrock or budget constraints, use of box culverts may be the solution. However, box culverts should not be used as a replacement for pipe culvert or for handling stream and water crossings.

➤ Other options.

Other water channeling devices include deflectors and log channel culvert. Water deflectors as used by the U.S. Forest Service are constructed by attaching wooden boards to either side of a long thick rubber conveyor belt and laying the unit edgewise into and across the road's surface. The exposed rubber belt portion remains approximately three inches (8 cm) above the road surface and acts to catch and convey runoff across the road. Vehicles can safely drive across the rubber deflector portion, as it remains flexible enough to bend and then return to its upright position after a vehicle has passed. When constructing and installing a deflector, be sure to keep the top of the wooden boards at least three inches (8 cm) below the road's surface. This leaves a total of approximately six inches (16 cm) of rubber belt to freely bend and flex with traffic. Also remember that deflectors in a road may be susceptible to damage due to grading and snowplow activity.

Cheap and easy to install, primitive log culverts act in similar fashion to box culverts with a few exceptions. Due to irregularities in log taper, radius, and alignment, they tend to readily catch loose debris and silt more quickly than other culvert options. Being round, log culverts are prone to spin when subjected to tire and vehicle movement. Provided they are constructed properly, their life span is only as good as the log species' resistance to decay and wear. As with box culverts, log culverts should not be used as a replacement for pipe culvert or for handling stream and water crossings.

✓ More "Do's"

- Be prepared to unearth anything.

- When purchasing road construction materials, seek longevity.

- Understand that versatile equipment is cost-effective equipment.

- When possible, plan roadwork to occur during dry and warm weather.

- Given a choice, it's better to have too much equipment than too little.

- Choose heavy equipment according to your task, location, and budget.

- Research desirable construction materials and determine their availability.

- As a rule, the sooner you act in restoring your roadway, the cheaper it will be.

- Clearly understand the terms and costs for returning unused construction materials.

- Examine all delivered materials and ensure that you're getting what you've paid for.

- Used materials may work fine but, unless they're heavily discounted, the risk in using them again may not be worth the gamble.

CHAPTER 6

Working with Your Neighbors

Almost In-laws.

Neighbors living on the same roadway can almost be viewed of as being unwillingly bound by marriage. They are tied together through good and bad until sale of real estate do them part.

Well it's not quite that bad, but many neighbors have been driven apart due to conflict over commonly owned roads.

With private roadways, adjoining landowners usually have a deeded right to use the road whether or not they help maintain it. It's a vested privilege, grandfathered with title. Unfortunately for many, equity-in-use does not translate into fair and equitable joint responsibility.

The trick to succeeding with your neighbors is to get them involved early and keep them involved as much as possible. It's a challenge to pull people together who have differing beliefs and varying levels of financial resource. Getting these same people to agree and follow through on a course of action may seem inconceivable. This is one reason why neighbors should avoid acting on the desires of a few wealthy neighbors and then billing everyone later for whatever cost it took to meet those desires.

Landowners with vision and the means to pull it off must work to include input from *everyone* living on or using the road. To have any hope of getting to consensus, everyone's roadway needs must be considered within the limits of the group's resources. If certain individuals can afford more or want to contribute more, that's fine, but a key ingredient towards building consensus involves getting everyone's contribution. Like family, almost.

Beginning the Road Association Process

➤ The house meeting.

As a group of neighbors, you'll need an agreement to agree. The process of formulating a base agenda can begin over a cordial pot of java anywhere, but usually happens in the home of one of the landowners. Set a time that is convenient for everyone. If that means moving the date further into the future to accommodate more landowners, do it. If it means meeting on a weekday evening or some time inconvenient for you, do it. It's worth it. Figure 6-1 suggests one of many possible scenarios where landowners organize and decide upon a course of action.

Beforehand, assign someone the task of controlling the heat of the meeting should ultraspirited debate or open conflict arise. After all, you will be freely discussing ways and options on spending your neighbors' money. The conversation may turn to somebody's poor driving habits or criticism of a prized vehicle. Or you may discuss an adjoining landowner's cattle, a neighbor's recent home remodeling traffic, or whom the garbage truck comes for and whom it doesn't come for. It's all open game and it should all be openly discussed.

This talk has to be closely controlled. You may even pre-script how and what gets discussed when dealing with challenging or volatile neighbors. Landowners who are alienated or made to feel bad at the initial meeting may not participate going forward. Others can be made to feel indifferent to what is happening and how the process is being managed. Neighbors who feel scorned will be less likely to support a road restoration project. This is not what you want. It is not what you had intended to happen. Work to avoid it.

Landowner Communication and Process

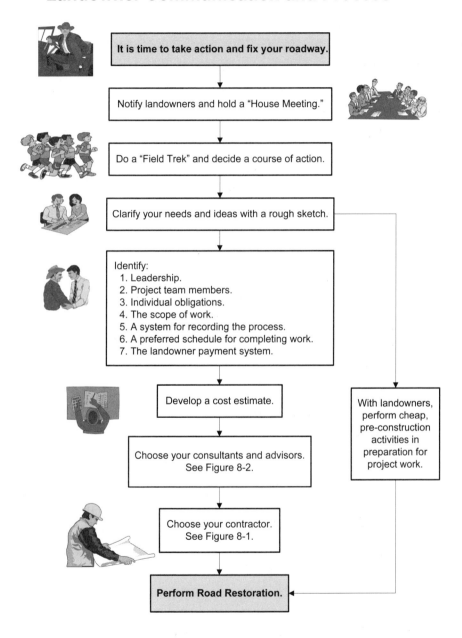

It is time to take action and fix your roadway.

Notify landowners and hold a "House Meeting."

Do a "Field Trek" and decide a course of action.

Clarify your needs and ideas with a rough sketch.

Identify:
1. Leadership.
2. Project team members.
3. Individual obligations.
4. The scope of work.
5. A system for recording the process.
6. A preferred schedule for completing work.
7. The landowner payment system.

Develop a cost estimate.

Choose your consultants and advisors.
See Figure 8-2.

With landowners, perform cheap, pre-construction activities in preparation for project work.

Choose your contractor.
See Figure 8-1.

Perform Road Restoration.

Figure 6-1. Landowners coming together.

Above all, be respectful, sensitive, and courteous.

With all attendees sitting around, invite them to introduce themselves to each other. Then, slowly begin an open discussion about the problems and condition of your roadway. What needs to be fixed? Have any accidents or mishaps occurred that can be used to help galvanize the group? Does everyone agree that the road has problems and what those problems are? As can be expected, the person living at the far end of the road will probably have something different to say than the person living at the beginning of the road.

For instance, those who travel the entire road will be more vocal concerning the roadway's surface deterioration than those who drive a short distance of the road. They will better notice all potholes, lack of drainage, and driveway problems. Those who travel short distances of the road will probably be more concerned with sight distance, vehicle speed, and dust. The key is to find common solutions that fit everyone's needs without losing sight of how they all relate to the long-term health of your road.

Regardless of how the discussions fall out, plan on doing all or some form of roadway restoration throughout the entire roadway at the same time. This tactic sends the message that:

1. Everyone needs to get something out of the process as soon as possible.

2. All neighbors need to know that their concerns and sense of urgency have equal weight.

3. Depending on how neighbors are charged, people who get their needs met at the beginning of the road may be less prone to want to pay for restoration later beyond their driveway, where it indirectly affects them. It may be okay by them if the person at the rear of the roadway helps pay for a portion of restoration up to and including their driveway, but they may be slow to help pay for improvements further back, towards the rear of the road.

So, what's the best approach to paying for this work? Equal or weighed cost sharing? Or, do you settle for whatever your neighbors can pay and only complete as much work as you can? Is there a right answer? It depends on how extensive your road restoration project is and how many neighbors can be relied upon to help foot the bill. What do you and your neighbors' value? Aesthetics, safety, or longevity? Discuss these issues. With enough planning and money, you can have it all but not unless people come together.

While taking copious notes, somebody, perhaps an appointed secretary, should begin to "connect the dots" as to what everyone's concerns are. Coincidental concerns and common gripes should be grouped as priority items for immediate attention. This includes obvious problems, safety hazards, and everyday nuisances. Try to serve the most people up front and in doing so, you'll build group momentum. Isolated issues that affect fewer people can be shelved for "phase-two" work, or put off for further discussion, but they cannot be forgotten unless resources allow them to be addressed with all immediate issues.

As in any important meeting, collect everyone's name, address, and phone number for distribution and recordkeeping. Repeat this process during all subsequent meetings.

➤ The field trek.

The next step is for everyone to collectively walk the roadway and visually inspect examples of roadway deterioration. Does your notion of damage and need for repair and restoration match your neighbors'? Is everyone on the same page? This is a crucial move since most people who never get out of their vehicles tend to be completely surprised at the poor condition of the roadway under their wheels.

The field trekkers are the select group of individuals that you want to target for participation. They may have seen no reason to review the road's condition but their presence indicates that they care. Caring people usually have leadership qualities that can help in rounding up the majority. This group also represents the people that you will most likely be able to count on for physical, mental, and financial support.

The field trek is a good time to inspect the culverts and ditch lines for water blockages. As an educational tool, have everyone get down and view the culvert opening. Most people have no idea that these things exist. Once they see the purpose and function of culverts, people understand the need to maintain them. If you are fortunate, someone may even volunteer to return later with a pitchfork and clean the culvert or ditchline of debris. Amazing things can happen on the field trek. More amazing things can happen with ten minutes of pitchfork work.

➤ Getting to yes.

Reaching a final determination that meets with most everyone's approval results from solid communication and educated planning. I say "most everyone" because it is difficult enough to get all neighbors and landowners to meet, let alone attain solidarity in financial budgeting.

For meetings to succeed, you must establish a distinct mission or substantive goal that clearly justifies spending everyone's time and money. Begin with a detail or rough plan showing what work needs to be done and where. It need not be to scale or pretty, though it must be functional and complete. See Figure A-1 in Appendix A titled, the *Robinswood Drive Proposed Road Restoration Plan*. Note that everyone must be able to orient themselves and feel as though they fully understand all the issues. A detailed drawing or plan helps accomplish he following:

- A drawing is a record. It works for and protects everyone.

- A drawing is the basis for any contractor bid or cost estimate.

- Graphics and pictures work well in communicating issues and problems.

- A drawing provides you and others one platform to download ideas and problem areas onto.

- A drawing makes it easier to visualize construction and scheduling complications relative to other people's property.

Beware of "willy-nilly" or "let's see what happens" attitudes. If a weekend warrior with his own ideas and equipment takes control of the group's efforts, people should ask, who is going to watch him? Is he looking to make a buck, only serve himself, or just have fun?

If this same neighbor is charging for his time and machinery, it is mandatory that his costs and scope of work be controlled from the beginning. If this person is performing work out of concern for his neighbors and is not charging or asking for financial reimbursement, be thankful. However, inspect that he is not further damaging the road or worsening previous conditions. Sometimes, free services are more trouble than they are worth.

If this person knows what he is doing while using his own equipment to perform roadway repairs, be sure to thank him for his effort. Offer to pay him at market rate for his time and resources. If he refuses due to his good nature or neighborly attitude, record the hours and what he accomplished. You can later get him a gift or have an after-project party or barbeque where awards and gratitudes can be distributed. Don't let any volunteer work go unnoticed and don't take such work for granted.

Conversely, if the group can't trust the weekend warrior and a conflict arises, it may poison any future involvement with this neighbor. When people sour in road associations, they rarely come back to the fold. Better strategies lie in channeling the weekend warrior's efforts than defeating them. There is wisdom in capturing everyone's attention and dedication the first time around, including the warrior's.

Keep both eyes wide open if you experience a weekend warrior. At least until you feel comfortable with his ability, intent, and actions.

Establishing a Road Association

A road "association" can take several forms. It can embody anything from a casual handshake to a formal legal entity. It can be short-lived and formulated for the sole and expressed reason to construct a project, which upon completion, expires. Or, as is usually the case, it can be written as a permanent, long-term, and binding agreement. It can be developed as a tool for collecting maintenance and repair monies or as a charter, used to cultivate order and procedures for those who travel the road.

Think about your objectives and what you're dealing with. Are you trying to organize people for the sake of building a project or are you driven by a desire to bring neighbors together? Do you have financial, legal, or vehicle safety concerns? Of course, you'll want to meet with an attorney when it's time to form an association, but be prepared before you meet. List your objectives, issues, and fears. If possible, meet with an attorney onsite or, at least, bring ample pictures of your road so that the attorney gets a feel for your situation.

The level and type of association that you choose can depend upon many factors unique to your neighborhood. However, one or more of the following items usually plays into how you build a road association:

1. Your group's gross finances.

2. Your need for liability protection.

3. Number of participating landowners.

4. The character, location, and condition of your roadway.

5. The mixture of people within your group (its chemistry).

6. Your road's proximity to environmentally sensitive areas.

7. Your project cost if you're constructing or repairing your roadway.

8. The extent of existing and the potential for future development in and around your roadway.

Informal and loose agreements may work fine under certain conditions but, as complications arise and the number of participants expands, the exposure to liability increases. Attorneys often recommend forming an L.L.C. or Limited Liability Company or, a non-profit corporation to limit liability and provide a formal process for decision-making. Liability protection for everyone increases when road repairs and improvements are planned, paid-for, and executed as a separate, formal entity. Otherwise, good-intentioned and diligent actions that alter the road's character enough to create unfamiliar changes and undue hazards, whether real or perceived, can result in exposing individuals to personal liability.

Road associations can be as formal as you desire. Listing from informal to most formal, here are some options that people have chosen to implement and operate under:

- No communication. Anyone does what he believes is appropriate.
- Verbal agreements.
- An in-house, non-binding written declaration of rules and procedures.
- An in-house, written and signed agreement.
- A limited liability company, non-profit corporation, or limited partnership.
- Protective covenants, conditions, and restrictions held by the association or within deeds of trust and conditions of ownership.

The waters of potential liability and landowner intent can be deep and murky. Organizing as a legal entity is highly recommended for both protection and for tax purposes. As you would expect, retain a qualified land-use attorney for both counsel and for drafting agreements related to forming your road association.

Working Together as a Road Association

You need to pursue working as a road association on everything and anything you can! Whether or not an official, legally binding document is drawn up depends on each association's particular situation. If you have access to free or reasonably priced, land-oriented legal advice, take it and share it with other neighbors.

The following menu is a good place to begin in helping to determine the backup information that you and your neighbors may require for legally documenting a joint road restoration agreement. Of course, depending upon the nature of your project, this stage of work also includes hiring an attorney and possibly an accountant, contractor, or other consultants.

➤ Gross dollar budget amount.

How much of your neighbor's financial commitment are you willing to accept based solely on trust and a handshake? Over the life of the project, what construction will happen and at what cost per year? How much money will you ultimately need? If the bottom falls out, can you and a small number of neighbors cover the cost of work without going to court to collect from delinquent neighbors? Identify worst case costs for permits, materials, construction, and consultants, including a contingency for poor weather and surprises during work. This will be your gross dollar budget amount.

• Number of participants and special interests.

How well do you know everyone? Can you manage the situation or are there too many individual interests? Are there landowners in the process of selling, moving, or building? How many cars and trucks use the roadway daily? Attach plat and land ownership maps to any agreement or contract in order to document who should participate and who benefits from the work.

• **Scope or extent of required work.**

What is involved? Do you need any bridges or retaining walls? Do you need a mile of asphalt, extensive excavations, or is work limited to minor pothole repair? Is there one overriding goal that everyone can agree upon? To complete the scope of work description, you'll need a construction plan of action, work schedule, and a list of milestones for completion.

• **Number of contractors and consultants involved.**

Large and complicated projects mean dealing with lots of people. Do you have enough time to handle coordinating the project (usually during weekdays) AND collecting neighbor payments and dues? If not, who will handle what? How will you spread accountability and responsibility?

Knowing who and what you'll need helps in deciding who and what you hire. Once all parties are identified, include their license, registration, and professional numbers as well as copies of any subcontracts, or special conditions as part of your agreement.

• **Are there any "heavy hitters" on deck?**

Do you foresee any development that might occur on the heels of fixing up your roadway? Is anyone getting a free ride that shouldn't get one? Will any commercial interests or public works projects follow your restoration that could threaten or undermine your work? You do not want to waste your time and money on a project that may be torn up within a short time and replaced with a higher-grade road by someone else. Sure, getting a better road is always good news, especially if it's free, but why put yourself through something like road construction if you don't have to?

• **Environmental and liability exposure.**

Could something go wrong? If so, identify where and how? If something does go wrong, who is liable? You, personally, or an organization bound by legal agreement? If you think for a second that you may have exposure here, get the opinion of a professional.

• Use limits.

What speed limit and use restrictions can everyone agree to? Are certain vehicles outlawed from using the road? Identify post-construction vehicle regulations and limitations. Clearly spell out how they will be enforced and policed.

Agreeing on Technical Items

Focus on what *needs* to be accomplished and *how* it gets accomplished. Then explain the process in clear and simple terms so that all your neighbors can understand it. This includes an understanding of construction terminology and the landowner's responsibility as documented in the contractor's agreement.

Although some landowners couldn't care less about how the road gets fixed as long as it gets fixed, they should have the option of being heard while the planning process evolves. Keeping your neighbors informed establishes history that you can lean on later should they not like what they see and attempt to hold you accountable. Distill your neighbors' opinions and requirements into a document, a reference for decision-making during construction and thereafter. This document should also define your neighbors' expectations and concerns. A laminated copy needs to be posted on the jobsite at all times for anyone to read.

When circulating plans, details, and agreed upon courses of action, ask for return signatures from all people involved as an acknowledgment of their approval and concurrence. Keep this information on record.

If your restoration efforts are a private issue with no regard for public or municipal road building standards, permits, or inspection, the task of directing and approving design and construction will fall on either someone in your neighborhood or a consultant.

➤ What type of roadway improvements can we do without majority support?

The following items do not require great sums of money nor do they require the services of a contractor:

- Dust control.
- Cutting brush.
- Erecting signs.
- Ditch cleaning.
- Filling potholes.
- Seeding and plantings.

➤ What type of roadway improvements should require majority support?

Examples of items that should require majority support include the following:

- Work that impedes traffic and access.
- Moving or altering mailboxes and garbage can collection locations.
- Improvements that alter drainage into or away from a neighbor's property.
- Anything that detracts from the value or appearance of someone's property.
- Higher-cost improvements such as grading, surfacing, and drainage structures.
- Any item that an inattentive, uninformed, or malicious neighbor can damage such as fresh surfacing or ditch protection.
- Improvements that can result in boundary disputes or ownership conflict such as fence disturbances, waste and borrow areas, and landscape impact.

- Items that can affect a neighbor's access such as elevation changes along the road as it fronts his land, added lips and drop-offs resulting from frontage to driveway transition grading, and new driver line-of-sight encumbrances.

➤ Technical particulars for everyone.

Refer to Figure 6-2. Once you and your neighbors have decided on a course of action, a structure for decision-making and "management" must be developed. As the design and planning phase for reconstruction transpires, it is a wise idea to make the following information clear and available to all landowners:

1. Identify leadership.

Once the association agrees to commit to construction, authority must be granted to an individual leader or small group of neighbors. This person or core group's responsibility is to establish direction, decisions, and oversight before, during, and after construction. Your leadership entity is still part of yet a bigger "project team" that includes your contractor, civil engineer, and whomever else you desire to help keep your project

Activity Schedule Prior to Construction

Possible Monthly and Weekly Schedule

Landowner Activity	Duration	March				April				May				June			
		1	2	3	4	1	2	3	4	1	2	3	4	1	2	3	4
Decide to Do Something	1 Day	■															
Alert Landowners to the House Meeting	3 Weeks		■														
Hold the House Meeting	1 Day				■												
Take the Field Trek, Identify a Course of Action	1 Day					■											
Contact Consultants	2 Weeks						■										
Develop the Construction Cost Estimate	3 Weeks							■									
Contact an Attorney	1 Week									■							
Contact and Interview Contractors	2 Weeks										■						
Bid/ Negotiate with Consultants and Contractors	3 Weeks												■				
Finalize Contracts	2 Weeks															■	
Set a Date to Begin Work	1 Day																■

Figure 6-2. Activity schedule prior to construction.

on track. Your leaders may already be defined within the association's agreement.

As the project progresses, changes and decisions may have to be made quickly. For instance, the plans and documents may be lacking or short on specifics, or a change of ground conditions may require your contractor to stop work and wait for direction. Leadership must be granted the power to intervene and, where appropriate, "fill in the blanks" as they see fit.

Consultants, contractors, and public agencies will also want to know who the point people are. They want to know who is empowered in case they get into a difficult situation or need to confer with someone of authority.

Do not usurp the decisions or judgment of your leader or leadership team unless you and your neighbors have very good reason in doing so. Nothing quite kills the volunteer spirit quicker than diluting someone's authority or exhibiting a feeling of unappreciation and mistrust. Carefully measure your actions before meddling with your contractor or project team and by all means, do whatever it takes to avoid decision-making by committee.

2. Set-up a field record system.

Tight recordkeeping includes maintaining a daily project diary. Examples of useful information to note in a daily diary include the following:

- Note the weather.

- Note when the contractor begins and ends work.

- Note changes in ground conditions and scope of work.

- Note any and all problems pertaining to that day's work.

- Note the contractor's equipment and hours used per piece.

- Take lots of pictures or video and back up all details in writing.

- Record which consultants showed up, why they came, and their hours.

- Meeting notes should include times, locations, participants, and content.

- Note material deliveries including the date, condition, and amount delivered.

- Record conversations, directions given, and the reasons for direction as given.

- Note excerpts and decisions made during conversations with the project team, public officials, and contractors.

- When the project is complete, make and distribute copies to all team members but store the original diary in a safe deposit box.

Copy the diary regularly and make these copies available in a weatherproof box. Neighbors can then pick up and read copies at their leisure, as the project matures. It's always good policy to inform everyone throughout the process as best as you can.

3. Identify where repairs and reconstruction is to transpire.

Stake or flag the construction zone areas in the field so all landowners can review the limits of work. Distribute a plan or map to everyone that shows these locations with a description of what work is planned along the route.

4. Specify the specifications.

If you do not have engineered plan sets to hand out, distribute a memo to everyone explaining what the construction specifications and dimensions will be. Include items such as depth and type of crushed rock surfacing, paving thickness, and number of new signs to be erected. If possible, sketch drawings of both plan and profile (top and side) views of the work as planned. Indicate where the contractor's materials and equipment will be stored. In order to avoid water and soil contamination, pick a spot where the contractor can safely fuel and mechanic his equipment and note it on the drawing.

5. Include a construction schedule.

Inform everyone as to when construction will begin and end. Either you or your contractor can put a simple bar schedule together. Notice the construction bar schedule shown in Figure 6-3 as it correlates with Figure A-1, the *Robinswood Drive Proposed Road Restoration Plan,* contained in Appendix A. Describe hours of work and list the construction activities that are planned to happen on each day. Include critical milestones on the schedule.

6. The cost estimate.

Make the cost estimate known to all who want it. Distribute multiple copies and leave copies in the waterproof information box. As changes occur, update the estimate. Quality estimates can be used as a reference against which costing of change order work may be evaluated. Afterall, on

Robinswood Drive Roadway Construction Schedule

Possible Weekly and Daily Schedule

Construction Activity	Duration	Week 1					Week 2					Week 3				
		M	T	W	Th	F	M	T	W	Th	F	M	T	W	Th	F
Begin Work	1 Day	■														
Call in to the One-Call Utility System	3 Days	■	■	■												
Mobilize Equipment and Materials	1 Day		■													
Set Temporary Traffic Control Signs	1 Day			■												
Install Erosion Control, Swale Protection	2 Days				■	■										
Log, Remove Brush, Stumps, and Topsoil	2 Days					■	■									
Install Survey Control and Layout	1 Day						■									
Sawcut Hard Surfaces	1 Day							■								
Black Forest, Kingsgate Circle Culverts	2 Days								■	■						
Widen Seasonal Swale Culvert	1 Day										■					
Fix Potholes, Widen Road, Grade Turnouts	2 Days										■	■				
Install Fabric, Rock, Grade, Ditch Road	2 Days												■	■		
Clean Existing Culverts, Add New Signage	1 Day														■	
Complete Project, Contractor Walk-Through	2 Days														■	■

Figure 6-3. Robinswood Drive construction schedule.

most unimproved road projects, the scope of work may change but it's more likely to change relative to quantities of ongoing work as opposed to adding completely new and unexpected construction activity. Figure A-2 (or the metric version, Figure A-5) in Appendix A shows the *Robinswood Drive Restoration Cost Estimate.*

7. Individual obligations.

If the project's costs are not evenly distributed among participating neighbors, make all neighbors aware of each other's financial obligation to the project. People who travel greater distances over the roadway may be paying a larger share of the costs. It's everyone's business to know the facts. This isn't an issue if all neighbors pay the same.

It's good policy to inform all nonparticipating and absentee landowners of costs. They need to be aware of how much each participating landowner is contributing to fixing up *their* roadway. Include a report that lists who physically worked on the roadway and mention dates, costs, approximate number of hours, and tasks completed.

In addition, your neighbors have a right to know who contributed monetarily to the project. Whether or not they review such information is their business but a listing of contributions needs to be made available. They have a right to know who gave more than asked, who gave enough, and who gave what they could. They also have the right to know who gave absolutely nothing. Unless they're financially or physically unable, neighbors that refrain from offering monetary support *and* who openly abstain from volunteering services for road labor or maintenance work have in essence made their position clear. They'll use the road, they may abuse the road, and they'll capitalize on improvements to the road, but they'll leave the road costs and work to someone else. Even though it's their responsibility to share in road maintenance, they'll have no part of it.

Listing who gave what isn't a witch-hunt. Afterall, short of legal action, there is little recourse available towards those who renege on roadway obligations. Still, knowing who gave what can work to strengthen neighbor relations by bringing people closer together. It helps to establish common ground on which people can unite. A listing of contributions provides a platform from which those, who gave more money than asked can be recognized. It acknowledges those who believe in upholding their obligations. It also provides a means of remembering those, who in spite of financial hardship, still manage to contribute something to make the project work. In the end, it helps to define who your neighbors are, where their values lie, and, ultimately, what it takes to build a cohesive road association.

Another reason to list who gave what involves cost and revenue accounting. Your neighbors will expect a job-ending summary report detailing how the dollars added up, how they were spent, and how much, if any, remains. For those neighbors that have the resources but prefer not to give, they need to be made aware of the expense, burden, and time that their neighbors have invested on their behalf. For those who do not have the resources, physical ability, or who are unable to participate for reasons beyond their control, such a report will inform them as to what has transpired and give them an idea of the value added to their property.

Cash is sweet but sweat equity also counts as a method of contributing to the project. People who volunteer time, expertise, and equipment without payment have added value to the project. Equating dollars to sweat equity can be complicated but it's possible to do. Consider this approach and strive to keep it fair and simple. An example of a notice informing all landowners of a planned road maintenance workday is shown in Figure 6-4.

8. Payment options.

Options exist requiring individuals to pay according to use. Such options don't reduce gross project cost but they may save some landowners proportionately depending upon how much they use or travel the roadway. Other options more evenly spread the cost among landowners.

What is fair? Should everyone pay the same? Should the older widow who slowly drives a sedan with broken shock absorbers and bent rims pay the same as the young buck who slams the roadway in his one-ton, chrome-endowed, four-wheel drive monster truck?

Should the neighbor who commutes daily in his loaded dump truck pay the same amount as the individual who commutes to work on a bicycle?

What about the landowner who contracts onsite garbage pick-up twice a week? Should they pay the same as the landowner who composts, recycles, and then monthly takes everything else in her own vehicle to a municipal dump?

Tough questions indeed. At what point does logic and fairness evolve into a finger pointing session?

Perhaps one solution is to consider a plan that requires all landowners who travel across the restoration segment of the road to pay on a cost-share basis according to how many drivers live in each home. Another option is to require landowners to pay according to the number of licensed vehicles that leave their property and regularly travel the roadway.

Another perspective may be to have everyone pay according to the amount of lineal footage of roadway each private landowner uses. In other words, what is the distance from each landowner's driveway to the beginning of the roadway restoration project?

In simple terms, once the total cost for the project is calculated, the following methods can be used to determine cost sharing responsibilities, but keep in mind that the right method for collecting funds may not be the fairest method and vice versa:

• **Payment Option 1: Everyone pays the same.** This method works well for roads that have multiple connection points to public highways and other streets.

Divide the sum total cost of road restoration by the total number of landowner parcels using, or who have legal access to use, the road segment receiving restoration work. Each parcel or lot pays equally as calculated by dividing the total cost of construction by the total number of benefiting properties. This method does not discriminate between those who use the entire restored roadway or those who only use portions of it for daily travel.

• **Payment Option 2: Everyone pays by the number of drivers or vehicles per home.** The sum total road restoration cost gets divided by the total number of drivers or licensed vehicles per household that use the road. Using this method, *vacant lots and land* would get assigned one driver or vehicle per parcel regardless of parcel size or if anyone periodically traverses to or from these vacant parcels. The construction cost is simply divided by your choice of total number of drivers or vehicles at the time of construction.

Once the gross per unit cost is known for the entire roadway, the total cost per household is then determined by multiplying the unit cost times the number of drivers or vehicles per home. Each home or landowner would be then liable to pay according to maximum projected use.

This method may not be practical on roads where there is significant turnover in real estate or where a high percentage of raw land exists.

• **Payment Option 3: Everyone pays according to the lineal distance of roadway used.** This option can be applied when charging landowners for the actual lineal-footage of roadway used when traveled to and from their property.

Refer to Figures A-3 and A-4, *Robinswood Drive Cost Share Plan and Breakdown* in Appendix A of this book. To view the metric version of Figure A-4, see Figure A-6 in the appendix. There you'll find a cost share plan and spreadsheet containing each landowner's cost based upon his location on the road. Below, you can follow the step-by-step mathematical analysis used for figuring each landowner's cost as noted on the English inch-pound version spreadsheet:

1. Determine the total road construction cost. In this case, it's $38,722. (See cost estimate Figure A-2 or, for the metric version, see Figure A-5 in Appendix A).

Following in Appendix A, Figure A-4:

2. Determine the total lineal footage of roadway to be worked. In this case it's 2,190 feet.

3. Divide step 1 into step 2 and determine the cost per lineal foot. This value equals $17.68.

4. Divide the roadway into segments or measurable lengths of road construction that correlate with landowner driveway locations and roadway intersections. (Columns B & C)

5. Multiply step 3, cost per lineal foot, by the total feet per segment. (Column D)

6. Figure the total number of landowners served by *that* segment of roadway. (Column E)

7. Divide Column D by Column E to determine the cost per landowner per segment. (Column F)

8. By adding the individual segment costs up to and including the segment at any landowner's property, you can now determine the landowner's total cost share amount. For example, a landowner who owns property at segment D-E would be expected to pay a prorated amount equaling $594. The landowner at segment J-K would be expected to pay a prorated amount equaling $3,299. (Column G)

9. Columns H and I are for information only but they help in portraying the gross cost burden per road segment. In summary, columns H and I portray both landowner count and total cost.

As you can see, all 28 landowners pay $79 each within segment A-B. Beginning with segment B-C, 27 landowners pay $154 each except the landowner living on segment A-B who is through paying (and happy about it). The third segment is calculated as such and so on. Eventually, the owners who live the farthest down the road end up paying the most,

$5,862, since their prorated share of use is greater than other landowners before them.

Five things worth noting:

1. Rounding errors may slightly alter your numbers from the exhibit.

2. The same analysis can be applied using number of drivers or vehicles per landowner parcel.

3. A second, more intensive analysis can be employed by using weighed or actual costs per segment instead of a flat, average cost per lineal foot. Use of this option may not make sense if segment costs increase significantly towards the rear of the road thereby making those at the end of the road pay an otherwise unbearable portion of the total road's cost.

4. Payment Option 3 is easiest applied to dead-end roads where landowners have no choice but to travel the same route to the outside world. Multiple road outlets complicate the analysis and may render any final information useless.

5. Pursue vacant landowners and make them aware of any cost liability.

Please note that numbers contained in the metric versions may slightly deviate due to differences in rounding and approximation.

• **Payment Option 4: Collect what you can and go from there.** In truth, many people cannot afford what it takes to properly restore and surface a roadway. I'm not referring to those who *choose* not to participate but rather, those who plain and simple do not have the cash or equity to swing the deal. If you and your neighbors really want the whole job done, you may have to pay a disproportionate share of the cost, finish the project, and move on. This entails being financially ready and able to cover the final construction cost regardless of any shortfall in neighborhood funding.

Or, you can collect whatever you can and stretch it as far as it will go on the way to deciding how and where to spend it. Either way, it's a tough way to go and hard feelings may be at stake.

9. Time to pay.

Clearly define the policy and mechanics for collecting payments. Note the accepted forms for payment, schedule for payment or payments, and how extra project cost items will be handled. Take this opportunity to note other financial items such as when yearly dues are collected or when funding will be needed for future repair and maintenance work.

10. Who still owes us?

Ongoing road restoration work or prior work that has not been paid for should be accounted for in a memo to all neighbors. It's only fair that everyone knows who has paid and which neighbors are delinquent. A running spreadsheet detailing payment history per neighbor can be built and distributed on a regular basis. Any accountant can assist you with building a suitable financial spreadsheet.

11. Do what you have to do.

Road associations and neighbors differ as much as road projects themselves. So, don't look for a formula or "well-worn" path to pulling off a successful project. Not all roadway problems can be dealt with in the same manner. Many times, you'll have to "wing-it," hoping later that you've made the correct decision. In doing so, tailor information into the project memo as you see fit. When dealing with multitudes of different people, I have found it best to flood them with detail. Too much information is better than too little and after you get done answering all the questions, you'll be glad that you took the proactive route.

Who Will Handle the Money?

Meet with your neighbors and discuss collecting money. Share ideas and develop a policy. As a rule, no fewer than two neighbors, and preferably three, should be together to witness each other when collecting neighbor's money. Try to encourage the use of checks. When payments arrive, record all revenue and promptly issue receipts. Don't let it wait and sit around.

Neighborhood funds can be written to a road association or construction project account. Your local bank or credit union will be glad to open an account specifically for this purpose. It is not recommended that someone bankroll the operation and rely on collecting from neighbors after work is completed. For obvious reasons, the risk of not getting equitable payment from all private landowners is real—with potentially disastrous results.

The core project group should have an individual or treasurer responsible for collecting and recording all money transactions. With neighborhood consensus, retain extra monies collected in an interest-bearing account earmarked for future road maintenance. If you end up with a windfall in savings, leftover monies can be returned to landowners, used for purchasing additional signs or extra rock surfacing, or spent on an all-out, well-earned block party.

Usually, nobody wants to be a banker. Some landowners don't want an official road association with monthly dues, meetings, etc. All they want is a good, sound, reliable road and that's okay too.

Dealing without Full Neighborhood Participation

As odd as this may seem, some people are satisfied with potholes, open cavitation, and general roadway degradation. They simply don't welcome change. Others cannot afford to pay for road restoration. Some neighbors can pay only a limited amount of money while others may prefer to make payments. There are also select individuals who get used to watching others manually labor up and down the road on their behalf. Without contributing help or finances, they lose appreciation for what their neighbors accomplish and may actually begin to expect others to continue improving and maintaining their road for them. They can be short on appreciation, long on opinions, and chronic complainers.

Unless protective covenants are in place and are strictly enforced, getting neighbors involved is usually easier said than done. These covenants are also known as CC & R's or "Covenants, Conditions, and Restrictions."

In some cases, landowners have no choice but to participate in the cost of roadway maintenance due to protective covenants tied to the purchase of their land. To check on the CC & R's within your road association, check your title insurance policy. Most banks, loan institutions, and lenders require that access roads be kept in some respectable form as a condition of property ownership. The problem is that roadway covenants are rarely enforced.

Although legal options exist in forcing compliance with protective covenants, it is not usually the intent of neighbors to exercise them. Without the weight of bankers, mortgage companies, and lending institutions, it is very hard to force people to pay for something that they don't want to pay for. It can cost a great deal to attempt to legally bind your neighbors to honor their covenants, and whatever the cost may be, it may not be worth it. When leverage is available through the lending institution of an unwilling neighbor, such action may put at risk any relations that you currently enjoy with your neighbor.

Other instances involve dealing with speculative builders or renters. If they do not want to participate in upgrading the roadway, the cost involved in trying to force them into the fold may again not be worth the time and effort.

But building a good neighborhood goes beyond the CC & R's. How you reconcile road restoration depends more on the group's chemistry. For most private landowners, the hope is that all people living off their road will equally see the need for repairs and therefore welcome the chance to pitch in and improve their road.

Another problem arises when decreeing exactly what makes a roadway

High Park Road Association
Announcement

It is that time again. After two years, the roadway could use a good brushing out, the culverts need to be checked, and we've got some potholes to fix.

We are planning to gather as many neighbors as possible on Saturday, October 14 between the Chuck Filmore's driveway and the county road in order to:

1) **Cut brush & limbs back.**
2) **Remove unwanted trees and growth.**
3) **Trim weeds & rake out debris.**
4) **Load trimmings for haul off for burning.**
5) **If time permits, discuss association finances and future road needs.**

This should result in:

1) **Improving driver sight distance.**
2) **An increased and opened-up road surface.**
3) **A drier road surface, which will result in a better roadway.**

Helpful tools include: Gloves, Weed-eaters, Rakes, Hedge Clippers, Chainsaws, Pruning saws, Shovels, & anything else that cuts brush.

We plan on beginning work no later than 9am and if enough people are involved, we hope to be finished within 6 hours. Thanks for reading this. Hope to see you there!

**Any questions, please call Lee Ann @ 261-9536,
or Geoff @ 261-1780.**

Figure 6-4. Workday announcement.

respectable. If standards do not exist either in agreement or covenant form, what basis can anyone defer to when judging a road's condition? Some covenants are specific. Others are not. For instance, if covenants fail to define what minimum, acceptable road access criteria is to be maintained, such as grade, type of surfacing, and road width, how can you measure a road's condition? You can't without being subjective or by writing your own set of rules.

So, where private roadway standards don't exist, they must be developed. This leads you to a fork in decision-making. One fork defines standards that people want and the other fork leads to standards that they can afford. Taking one fork over the other may disinterest any number of neighbors. The art lies in finding a best-case compromise that suits as many people as possible.

If you elect to challenge your neighbor's decisions to not participate, be tactful. Seek them out face-to-face or at least call them. Don't begin the process as a letter writing campaign.

Once you have their attention, briefly lay out the plan and ask for their opinion. Listen to their concerns and reasoning. Try not to be judgmental or critical and stay clear of philosophical issues. Do not entice or play into confrontation. Instead, focus on why the road is falling apart and what it will take to improve it. Be fair to both your unwilling neighbor and be fair to yourself. After all, it's only a road and they may have a point of view that you hadn't yet considered.

As a last resort in dealing with landowners who refuse to meet their fair obligation, try to get whatever they are willing to give. A partial payment, volunteer work in trimming vegetation, anything is better than nothing combined with hard feelings. If the situation warrants legal action, consult an attorney.

It is important to remember that it will be slower and more difficult establishing road programs within developments having nonpaved roads and a surplus of remaining raw lots for sale.

Multiple remaining raw lots means new construction and future owners spread over an unspecified period of time. The resulting steady influx of real estate people and contractors means lots of heavy and fast travel. New lot owners may or may not be eager to sign on to a road maintenance program. Their primary concern will be permits, home construction, and budgets. Until most of the lots are built upon, and people occupy them, brace yourself for disjointed cooperation and less available money per lot for roadway maintenance work.

We Can't Afford This Now. What Can We Do?

Prepare your neighbors. Begin talking with them immediately. Send suggestions, plans, and correspondence to all absentee landowners. Keep everyone informed. Comprise a plan at least six months before you plan to begin roadway restoration.

Given time, landowners may discover that they can budget enough funds to cover their fair portion of work. Time also allows them to cool off if they are adamantly opposed to spending a dime. If after contacting everyone and sending out construction plans, you do not receive enough responses, you may be forced to work with whatever funds and volunteer efforts materialize. Less money may force you into deciding which work absolutely needs to be addressed. Other options may include not working sections of roadway where support is lacking, paving one narrow 11-foot (335 cm) lane, or pursuing short-term fixes as covered in Chapter 2.

It is important to stress and make clear to all neighbors that complete roadway restoration will cost more money up front. However, in the long run, doing it right saves money over the life of the road and works to reduce everyone's time and stress later.

Boundary Disputes

Boundary disputes can stall or kill roadway restoration. This problem becomes more acute as acreages become steeper in slope or as lots become smaller and homes get closer to each other. They also become more prevalent with older properties where survey evidence does not exist or is suspect. Property boundaries, fences, and existing roadways may infringe unknowingly on another person's land.

Of course, boundary disputes increase among people who yearn for conflict while possessing the financial means to support such battles.

Although boundary disputes can involve personalities, agendas, and people flat-out wrong, boundary delineation is backed in law. The most effective way to begin dealing with these problems is to engage all parties in fair and honest, open communication.

Initially, it's recommended that you contact the respective title companies and obtain copies of the properties' legal descriptions. Next, obtain a copy of the survey records for each property in question. Upon comparing both the survey and legal descriptions, note any discrepancies. If a survey record does not exist, you may have to mutually agree as to where the line exists and end the dispute there or summon an official survey.

If survey records exist, with your neighbor, walk the property and look for survey markers and monumentation. Try to get a general feel for the surveys as they relate to both properties. This may involve hiring a surveyor to assist or even renting a metal detector to help locate metal stakes that may be buried or obstructed from view.

Once you have field-checked the surveys, obvious and easily explained differences may be apparent. If so, try to work them out with your neighbor before going further. This may entail pursuing a lot line adjustment agreement, thus correcting the problem with minimal legal and survey cost to both parties.

If a discrepancy exists between actual *surveys*, petition the surveyors involved and research any differences in the surveys. Did both surveyors use the same starting point? Which survey has more credence, the older original survey or the more modern survey? Irreconcilable technical differences and hard dealings between dueling surveyors may again be remedied with a simple lot line adjustment agreement.

If continued problems remain, forcing you into court, he who presents the best case usually wins. In boundary disputes, winning can be largely governed by the quality and accuracy of both the original legal description and survey.

Another factor called "adverse possession" may also come into play. Adverse possession means that whomever can demonstrate that they have used or encroached on land for an extended period of years may get clear title to that land regardless of whom legally, by title or description owns that land. Use constitutes openly, and without permission, imposing a physical presence (such as a fence, roadway, or structure) on someone else's property. Laws and circumstances vary from state to state so it's best to rely on an attorney for accurate and specific information.

Messy encounters involving attorneys and court experiences usually permanently end one or both party's involvement in neighborhood roadway projects. They learn to live with the road's condition the way it exists.

As a tip, remember that people seem to get along when fair and clear property boundaries are established. Fencing property and denoting public or common right-of-ways and easements is a good way to avoid boundary disputes. If a dispute can't be avoided, promptly seek counsel from a qualified land-use attorney.

➤ What if a ditchline or portion of roadway exists on my property? How do I handle a neighbor who, against my will, continues to cross onto my land in order to perform roadway work?

If a ditch or roadway portion is jointly owned, both parties should agree in writing how and when maintenance should be performed. If portions of the existing road are actually on your property without legal consent in the form of an easement or right-of-way grant, nobody has the right to trespass without permission. Have the property in question professionally surveyed. If the survey supports your position that the roadway is in fact illegally on your property, you alternatives include the following:

• **Fight it.** Continue to keep *No Trespassing* signs up and prohibit anyone from accessing your property. This will ultimately result in bad neighbor relations and perhaps a civil challenge. Be the first one to seek the advice of a land attorney if the survey shows the road right-of-way being on your property.

• **Look the other way.** In the name of maintaining cordial neighborly relations, agree in writing to allow roadway maintenance to proceed without your permission. This may require professional mediation if you cannot otherwise agree with your neighbor.

• **Legally bind it.** If they do not already exist, pursue blanket or reciprocal roadway easements with your neighbors that grant everyone access and maintenance rights over your roadway. Be sure that the easement allows only for an access road and no other personal land features such as fences, tool sheds, or driveway gates. The easement will have to be legally described and recorded. You will need to have the easement surveyed and located in the field. Hire an attorney when dealing with easement, right-of-way, and land-ownership issues and disputes.

• **Move the road.** If the roadway no longer exists in its legal location, you can pay to have it moved where it belongs. This involves first seeking legal representation. Do you have a case? If you do, contact your neighbor(s) and discuss options. One such option involves surveying and marking where the roadway should be and then, moving it to its described and recorded location. Other legal complications may arise concerning whose property you move it to, how you move it, what features get removed during the process, and the rights of your neighbors. Then there's the cost.

➤ Should adjoining landowners who don't use the road pay?

It's possible that some landowners have multiple ways to access their property. Either their property is so big that it borders more than one private road or they just don't use certain roads even though the road easements may cross their land. Should they share in road repair costs if they don't solely rely upon, or use the road? If they do share in paying a portion of the cost, how much could be expected from a non-use landowner with, say, a mile of easement and private road frontage that serves a small eight-lot subdivision at the end of the road—a subdivision that completely relies on the road and whose members want to pave it? What is fair and what is disproportionate? Above all, what does it take to keep and maintain good neighbor relations?

This can be a tough issue. Looking at it from a large landowner's perspective, they've already lost use of the land, they're paying taxes on the land, and a poor road, if nothing else, can result in dust, erosion, and an eyesore. It doesn't seem right that a non-user should have to pay maintenance fees against road damage that they've had no hand in creating. Unless of couse, they want to pay.

As opposed to on-going maintenance costs, it seems reasonable to expect non-users to contribute toward capital improvements that enhance the value of their property while improving their quality of life. Examples of capital improvements include paving, utilities and stubs, lighting, signage, ditch work, and landscaping. What each landowner pays depends upon the situation. But one thing is for sure, it all starts with open communication and it should end with a friendly handshake.

Remember, you could be liable for project-related injuries sustained on your property even though the project may be happening for the benefit and under the direction of both you and your neighbors! In matters concerning legal ownership and boundary disputes, always seek the advice of a qualified attorney.

✓ More "Do's"

- Value and consider all input.

- Make very few, if any, decisions by committee.

- Work to keep all meetings focused and on-track.

- Keep neighbors informed with plans and visual aids.

- Distribute meeting minutes promptly to all neighbors.

- Develop a quarterly or semi-annual road association newsletter.

- Seek the guidance of an attorney when creating a road association.

- Follow and closely monitor the group's revenue and cost situation.

- Post and distribute cost estimates and schedules once they are known.

- When tensions rise, remember it's neighbors first and the road second.

- Open a local bank account for your road association or neighbor group.

- Tread cautiously when encountering boundary and ownership disputes.

- Clearly mark property corners that could be affected by roadway construction.

- Determine who wants to operate, and who is qualified to operate, the equipment.

- Encourage that neighbors use the channels of authority as set forth by your team.

- Set up a complete and comprehensive recordkeeping and documentation system.

- Avoid demonstrative and overbearing behavior while working with your neighbors.

- If you own distant property, stay current on its condition, zoning, and land-use status.

- Take great care in planning the first open house meeting; it may be your only chance.

- Before pursuing disputes and legal wrangling with a neighbor, ask yourself, is it worth it?

- Collect, file, and make available copies of adjoining property surveys along the work zone.

- List priorities and multiple options for construction, depending on how much money is collected.

- Consider the fact that you may need a "Sugar Daddy" or group of neighbors who will pay the final bill should funding fall short.

- For one of your meetings, invite a local real estate agent to address the group and talk about road improvements and their effect on property valuations.

- If possible, collect and understand all neighbors' road maintenance agreements and any existing covenants, conditions, and restrictions (CC & R's) before finalizing your plans.

CHAPTER 7

Doing It Yourself

Choosing the Proper Equipment

Doing the work yourself begins with choosing the correct equipment. If you already own equipment, is it sufficient to perform what's needed? Although construction equipment can usually be stretched to perform multiple tasks, no piece of equipment can do it all. As a rule, construction equipment should only be used to perform work that it was intended for. Once you've exhausted the design capability for any piece of equipment, it's time to move on and rent specialized machinery in order to safely complete your task.

Since road restoration projects everywhere differ in scope and objective, no single list of equipment works for each group. Once you've decided upon your equipment needs, you'll find a menu of machinery options at local rental shops. Here are some things to understand when renting heavy equipment.

➤ **Renting equipment.**

First consider your location and budget before speculating about renting *any* machinery. Then ask yourself the following questions:

- Do they deliver?

- When is service *not* available?
- How will you fuel the equipment?
- Where is the nearest rental company?
- What is best for you and your project?
- How do they calculate billable hours and hours of use?
- How many rental companies do you have to choose from?
- What does each company offer and what are its policies?

Then check for equipment availability. Can you get what you need when you need it? If so, then what are your choices and what does it cost? It's recommended that you visit competing rental companies and inspect their gear. Talk to the people and look at their stock. Kick around the repair shop. What do you see and what's its condition? You can gauge a rental company by simply looking at the condition of its equipment.

Rental companies also deal, and they are more prone to deal, with someone whom they feel they can trust with their equipment. They may also offer you a better rate on multiple pieces of machinery or if you rent over an extended period of time. Inquire about getting newer equipment, or whether the rental company will give you a deal on larger equipment if it has an over-abundance of it sitting in the yard. Anything is open game when negotiating with a rental company.

Bear in mind that many rental companies actually *govern-down* or adjust the maximum power output lower on equipment rented to nonprofessionals. The power is reduced to a maximum safe level that won't damage the equipment if the machine is pushed to handle tasks beyond its designed capability. This helps to prevent novice operators or anyone, for that matter, from literally tearing the equipment apart because of inexperience, abuse, or carelessness. For this reason alone, you may want to consider renting equipment larger and more powerful than you think you need. Larger equipment also tends to be more versatile.

It's wise to purchase additional insurance, especially if multiple individuals will be operating the same equipment, or if you don't enjoy the services of a professional operator. If money is no object, purchase more insurance anyway. You can use as much protection and insurance as you can afford. To save yourself time and hassle later, maintain and protect rental equipment as though it were your own and follow the rental shop's rules for cleaning and refueling before returning it.

➤ Rubber-tired versus tracked equipment.

Once you have determined that multitudes of rental equipment await your project, it is time to take a closer look at specifics. While strolling through yards of rental equipment, you will notice that earthmoving options exist between using wheeled and tracked machinery. Rural landowners beware: research the bridges on the way to your property. Weight restrictions and bridge widths may hinder the size of equipment that can be transported to your project. Check with local highway departments or consult a civil engineer if you have any bridge capacity issues. Don't miss this one!

Provided same-sized pieces of equipment are identically outfitted with approximate equal power and weight, comparisons between rubber and tracks can be summed up as follows:

Rubber-tired equipment.

- Moves quicker.
- Is highway friendlier.
- Is generally cheaper to rent.
- Doesn't fare as well in mud and icy conditions.
- Is much easier on existing asphalt and concrete.
- Will find any soft spots in the subgrade quicker than a track machine.
- For most nonprofessionals, it's easier to operate than track equipment.

- Can be turned around on existing gravel driveways without excessive rutting and damage to the driveway surface.

Track equipment.

- Generally is more challenging to operate.
- Is more stable on side slopes and in ditches.
- Is generally preferable for grading operations.
- Provides better traction than rubber-tired equipment.
- Will perform better in snow, ice, and wet conditions.
- Requires longer cleaning time than rubber-tired equipment.
- Will "float" on unstable soils better than rubber-tired equipment.

➤ Compactors.

All contractors and do-it-yourselfers must choose the correct *compaction equipment*. Choice of equipment depends on your work application(s) *and* soil type(s). Compaction equipment that develops higher frequencies, around 6,000 vibrations per minute, is recommended for loose, granular soils and asphalt. Lower frequency equipment offering 3,500 vibrations per minute is preferred when compacting fine-grained and clay soils. In either case, the goal of compaction is to decrease soil voids, increase soil density, increase load-bearing capacity, and achieve overall soil stability.

Generally speaking, compaction equipment must first deliver centrifugal force. That is, it must strike hard against the ground. Secondly, compaction equipment must deliver a frequency in terms of vibrations per minute. Review these requirements with your rental dealer and consider recommendations from a local geotechnical consultant.

Options for compaction equipment break into two broad categories, namely, operator-driven or hand-operated (walk-behind). Specifying compaction equipment for your application should be dictated by the following *physical* variables:

- Your ability.
- Equipment size.

- Workspace area.
- Travel speed requirements.

As a rule, operator-driven equipment is more expensive to rent than hand-operated equipment. Being quite large, it is usually hauled by use of a trailer or lowboy. Let's explore operator-driven and hand-operated types of equipment in regard to various road construction work applications.

➤ Culvert, pipe trench, and ditch compaction.

For most culvert applications, pipe diameters will be less than 30 inches (750 mm). Typically, this size of pipe does not require a large trench excavation. Compaction equipment that works well for bedding pipe trenches includes the following:

• Small drum rollers.

Small single and double drum rollers are designed for working and compacting soil in confined areas. Single drum rollers are powered by a set of rear rubber tires. Double drum rollers have a steel drum on both the front and rear of the machine. For this reason, single drum rollers afford better traction, thus work better than double drum rollers on steeper slopes and grades.

Double drum rollers are more expensive to rent. They are also trickier to operate than a single drum compactor. Both styles of compactors are available in either static (nonshaking) or vibratory machines. When used in compacting trenches, both types of rollers require adequate trench access and enough working area to justify renting and transporting costs.

Consider using a small drum roller in a trench large enough for it to work in.

• Large multiuse vibratory rollers.

Large operator-driven rollers work in large trenches. They can also do double duty in trenches and on road surfaces, provided there is enough work to justify their expense.

However, they work best when compacting longer stretches of roadway that cover significant square area. When used as such, large rollers compact broad areas quickly and they are cost-effective. Vibratory rollers with rear pneumatic tires work well for "seating" crushed rock above subgrade. When used on hot asphalt, they produce a tighter textured pavement surface than non-vibratory (static) rollers. Vibratory rollers with rear tires will find and compact soft spots while double drum rollers tend to bridge soft areas.

Single and double drum compactors get stuck easily and can get away from an inattentive operator. If the engine quits, it is easy to lose control. Rollers are responsible for a significant number of fatalities each year and must be regarded with the utmost caution and respect. Ask about the condition of the brakes before you rent this type of machinery. If, while operating, you feel unsafe, get off it immediately and either use a different compaction method or hire a professional.

• Backhoe or Excavator operated tamps.

This alternative uses stationary construction equipment to reach and apply compactive effort. Commonly called a "hoe-pack," these machines achieve results by employing a compaction attachment on the end of an excavator arm. Although more expensive to rent than comparative roller compactors, these pieces of equipment are more versatile in that you can dig, load, or compact by simply changing attachments. Stationary compaction machines are limited to trench and ditch work (which they perform very well), and spot road surface compaction. They are not cost-effective or practical for entire subgrade or wholesale asphalt compaction. Vibratory tampers mounted on stationary equipment are preferred where safety concerns preclude sending anyone into the trench to perform on-grade compaction.

The terms backhoe and excavator are used loosely in the construction industry in describing the same equipment. That is, a mobile, swing type machine that digs by means of an extended, hydraulically operated arm.

I like to think of backhoes as being rubber-tired and excavators as being track machinery. Most heavy equipment manufacturers label their larger digging machines as excavators, as opposed to farmers, who predominantly use rubber-tired machinery and tend to call such equipment backhoes. The point is, you have a choice between track and rubber-tired equipment when renting a hoe-pack.

• A walk behind plate compactor.

Small, manual, walk-behind, plate compactors work best on small jobs and in confined areas. They are easy on the budget and long on physical labor. Plate compactors result in slower production when compared to fully operated machinery but they are easy to maneuver and the resulting compaction is usually adequate for small repairs, sidewalks, and pipe backfill. Be sure to get one that goes in reverse, saving you the need to physically move the machine when turning.

• Jumping-jack rammers.

Ideally suited for the "macho" in all of us, these units can be somewhat dangerous to the uninitiated. Jumping-jacks work by ramming up and down on your subject, in similar fashion to a piston. They're easy to maneuver but take some getting used to. Preferred applications are in small areas where maneuverability is at a premium. Experienced operators, please.

• Remote controlled compactors.

Unless you have cash to burn or pine for high-tech entertainment, these units are not recommended for the average road association. If, however, your culvert is quite deep and the trench slopes are not stable, a remote controlled unit may be the only *safe* way to compact the trench bottom without putting someone's life or limb at risk. Under such conditions, a hoe-pack may provide you with an effective alternative.

• **Subgrade and rock compaction.**

If a geotechnical or civil engineer is responsible for recommending compaction standards for your roadway, be sure you get and understand the following information:

1. Type of soils.

2. Current soil moisture content.

3. Maximum thickness of compaction lifts.

4. Number of required compaction lifts.

5. Where compaction is and is not required.

6. Target density to be attained by compaction.

Working road base soils to these parameters is highly recommended for extensive road jobs or when holding a contractor to measured design specifications. If you want your local public jurisdiction to take future ownership and maintenance of your roadway, you will need geotechnical records proving that you constructed to acceptable soil standards. Geotechnical standards are meant to guarantee quality. Quality translates to longevity.

If you are working under a public agency permit, having this information in some form or another will likely be mandatory as a condition of construction.

Soils and Their Effect on Choosing Compaction Equipment

Soils and the type of fill material that you use should influence your choice in compaction equipment. Hand-operated compaction equipment works best on soils that are easier to manipulate. However, manually operated methods don't generate the force and consolidation that heavy equipment offers when dealing with sticky and fine-grained soils.

Consult with a local contractor or geotechnical engineer to better understand your options. Here are some general guidelines for choosing compaction equipment relative to soil type encountered:

- **Sheepsfoot roller.** Best used on silty and clay soils.

- **Two-drum articulated vibratory roller.** Versatile on crushed rock, gravels, clay, mixed soils, silts, and asphalt mix.

- **Single-drum roller.** Use on crushed rock, gravel, and asphalt mix.

- **Walk-behind vibratory plate.** Best used on sand, gravel, drain rock, silt, clay, and mixed granular soils.

- **Hand-operated, jumping-jack rammer.** Best used on gravel, silt, drain rock, and mixed granular soils.

Renting Equipment with Special Accessories and Attachments

Should you consider renting equipment with special attachments? *Definitely.* If you need to reshape your existing roadway, a bulldozer can dig, grade, and rip the roadway. For ripping, rent a dozer with ripper teeth sufficient to dig at least eight inches (20 cm) deep.

Bulldozers are available with a variety of blade attachments. If you are cutting, pushing, and moving a tremendous amount of dirt, consider a "U-shaped" blade. For grading, you'll want to specify a straight blade. If your roadway project is large enough, it may make sense to have two bulldozers on site, each with a different blade, or one bulldozer and two available blades. Winch attachments and brush rakes comes in handy if you are dealing with quantities of debris, logs, and stumps.

A large excavator can dig, load, backfill, rip, compact, and lift materials. In order to squeeze the most out of an excavator, rent one that has a bucket with hooks for lifting and teeth large enough for ripping the road's surface. Hooks are useful for lifting items such as culvert sections, signs, logs, and stumps. Be sure to also include cables or slings commensurate with the excavator's size and loads that you expect to encounter. Rent a machine with a bucket that is sized and shaped for optimal digging in the type of ground conditions that you expect. Other attachments including a compaction head and brush cutter may be recommended depending on your needs.

➤ Additional helpful pieces of equipment include:

- Hand-operated winch.
- Chain saws and pipe cutting saws.
- Chains with hooks and logging chokers.
- Rakes, square-tip and curved shovels, posthole diggers, and a pick.
- Ratchets and wrenches if you are installing galvanized or steel culvert.
- Hand and power saws, sharp knife, primer, glue, and clean rags if you are installing plastic pipe or culvert.

Installing Culverts

Culvert design, permitting, and installation are for professionals. Culvert planning and installation require an in-depth knowledge of water hydraulics, civil engineering, sensitive area issues involving water quality, fish habitat, and streamside protection, as well as construction know-how. While most culvert considerations can be left to the professionals, if you're dealing with reconstruction of or installation of culverts, here are some highlights to remember:

➤ Lay culverts in properly.

Culverts provide drainage. They relieve water and must be installed to drain *away* from the source of flow. Sounds elementary doesn't it? It is surprising how many contractors actually install pipes too flat, with a mid-span dip or hump, or with opposite fall.

Unless you adequately compact the soil under your culvert, you'll need to install the culvert with a very slight "bow" or arch upward, in the center of the trench where the heaviest traffic is to be expected. This traditional road-building practice is designed to compensate, beforehand, for any disproportionate soil settling that may occur directly under the pipe at road centerline as opposed to the ends of the pipe. Culverts should lie flat enough to pass water and not develop a low spot or belly that would hold and pond water. If this were to occur, water might be able to permeate through pipe joints and into the road subgrade.

The minimum depth of fill that should be placed above culverts varies. Depth of fill over culverts depends on culvert diameter, culvert material, quality of backfill, compaction standard, and type of road surfacing. Some standards claim that 12 to 18 inches (30 cm to 45 cm) is bare minimum, as any less may put you at risk of deforming or even crushing the culvert. It's best to inquire with your pipe supplier or manufacturer as to the minimum and maximum fill depths allowed when installing your culverts.

Culverts should extend no less than 12 inches (30 cm) beyond the road fill and be placed to accept water without allowing it a chance to soak into the subgrade. Roadways that act as dams allow water to pond and degrade the road's foundation. Keep water in the pipe or ditch. Nowhere else.

Solutions for channeling and containing flow can be found at pipe supply houses in the form of headwalls and channeled inlet pieces. Poured in place concrete and rock retaining walls are another method to assist in keeping water from infiltrating roadway subgrades. It's important that culverts neither cause nor perpetuate water sitting inside culverts or pooling where they empty out. Culverts should be high enough to guarantee continual passage and movement of water while acting to prohibit water from backing up into the culvert itself. As mentioned above, water sitting in a culvert can infiltrate pipe joints and find it's way into your road subgrade or in and around the culvert.

The quality of structural fill material that supports culvert bottoms, culvert sidewalls, and top cover is only going to be effective if properly placed and compacted. Fill material must be installed and compacted in layers (called lifts) usually not to exceed eight inches (20 cm) in depth. Regulated lifts allow ample opportunity for thorough compaction and culvert support. Poorly installed culverts can cause the pipe itself to accept loading and bridge unfilled areas. Unintended loads and unsupported pipes will eventually fail. Culverts and pipes must never be installed without continuous structural support.

Be sure that the roadway either drains to one side or is arched or "crowned" in the center so as to shed water runoff both ways into ditches and culverts.

Common Pitfalls and How to Avoid Them

Avoid the following pitfalls when performing road construction:

➤ Be cautious of the weekend warrior.

Neighbors who posses the skill and equipment to perform road improvements can be a blessing. In contrast, allowing a neighbor to perform work that he's not capable of completing either in scope or quality can lead to big problems. Unless your neighbor is a competent contractor, an experienced equipment operator, or has more than adequate resources to complete the job, it is best to avoid using him to perform road work.

Paying a little extra for a professional operator with equipment will not only get the job done, it will usually get the job done right. Construction workers and operators also have access to other equipment and excess materials that may prove invaluable if needed while working over holidays, weekends, and after-hours.

➤ Dig test holes (pothole) when in doubt.

If you, your road designer, or your contractor have suspicions as to what exists below the road's surface, dig down and investigate. Do this *before* setting budgets and contracts. Be sure to use the One-Call System before performing any digging activity. When you're done exploring, any holes should be filled and adequately compacted with dry, inorganic soil or crushed rock.

➤ Call BEFORE you dig.

Be familiar with and use the toll-free calling plan called the **One-Call System**. *One-Call Systems International Committee* (OCSI) is a worldwide system that has been specifically designed to avoid damaging existing utilities as a result of construction.

You must use this system prior to performing any digging.

Begin by calling into the system at least 48 hours or more *before digging* in order to alert them of your intent to dig. Upon calling the 1-800 toll-free number for your area, your project information will be recorded and passed on to both public and private utility agencies that own and maintain facilities in your project's vicinity.

Since utility damages can entail legal and financial consequences, your taped message(s) on the 1-800 number will become a document of record. If a utility line gets damaged, a record of this nature becomes helpful in sorting out the content of your initial information as it relates to subsequent responsibility for damages.

Underground utilities, may include all or some of the following:

- Gas.
- Power.
- Phone.
- Sewer.
- Water.
- Cable TV.
- Communication and data lines.
- Street lighting and signalization.

The American Public Works Association (APWA) would be happy to provide you with One-Call information in your area if you contact them at 816-472-6100.

Their standard color coding system for underground utilities are as follows:

- Blue—Potable water lines.
- Green—Sanitary, storm, and drain sewer systems.
- Red—Electrical power, lighting, and conduit lines.
- Orange—Communication utilities such as telephone, cable television, and signalization.
- Yellow—Fuel lines such as gas, fuel, steam, and oil. Steam may vary in color depending on the local utility.
- Pink—Temporary survey markings used by utility companies when locating their utility lines.
- Purple—Reclaimed water, irrigation, and slurry lines.
- White—The limits of proposed excavation.

Once contacted, utilities will field locate and mark their respective pipes, cables, conduit, or whatever they have in the ground with color-coded paint. In some instances, utilities will contact landowners or contractors to answer questions or provide additional information pertaining to their lines and vaults.

Record and document all utility markings prior to excavation by use of video and color photos. Note the depths and description of anything else below ground for both landowner records and contractor use. Include your own markings of any privately owned culverts, roof drain locations, home-owner installed cables, or anything else that isn't commonly known or of public record. Mark such anomalies and private facilities with a paint color *different* from any mentioned above.

If after your utility companies have marked their lines it rains, or their paint becomes faint, or you get delayed and allow their paint to completely fade, summon your utilities again or re-contact the One-Call System. Do not begin any work without having accurately re-marked utility locations.

Don't sweat the phone calls and crew time put in by the utility companies. At the time of this printing, one-call service is completely paid for by the utility companies themselves unless you proceed and break something without having used the system.

In that case, you may end up being fined and paying for damages. Damages might include paying for materials, contractor crew downtime, overtime, the cost of lost communication between utility users and so forth. In the most unfortunate incidents, lives could be lost or people could be severely injured due to explosion, electrocution, and fire. Ultimate consequences of not calling the One-Call System can equate to criminal charges and contractor or landowner bankruptcy. Suffice it to say, USE THE SYSTEM.

You may elect double protection by *directly* calling all local utility companies in addition to using the One-Call System. It is important to realize that not every utility company belongs to the One-Call System. Follow up with all local utility companies to be sure!

It's also a good idea to contact these companies during the planning stage so that you'll better know what you are dealing with. Don't wait until you have a contractor or rented equipment standing by, meters running and operators drinking coffee only to find out that you can't construct as planned. So, be wise and meet with these entities while planning your work. Share copies of your plan with neighbors, utility people, and contractors. White paint can be used to premark your intended area of construction before utilities arrive to mark their lines.

As discussed a few pages back, budget money for "potholing." Potholing is a construction procedure whereby contractors excavate slowly or use hand-digging methods in order to uncover and locate buried utilities before beginning contract work. By the way, all contractors should have their local 1-800 number and system directions posted on their construction equipment. If your contractor does not sport this information, suggest having them have post it (or require it) before allowing them to work on your project.

Contact all neighbors who might be impacted adversely if a power outage or utility failure were to occur, *especially the elderly and infirm!*

➤ Another tax payment?

Most people who perform private roadwork overlook the area where public pavement and right-of-way adjoins private property. Do not overlook this transition point for the following reasons:

- The line separating public and private roadways delineates which pocket pays for roadwork. On one side, you pay for roadwork via taxes. On the private side, you pay for roadwork with after-tax (take-home) money.

- You don't want to be liable for accidentally working on public property without permission.

- You don't want to perform work on public property without a permit or below the standards for such work as imposed by the controlling municipality.

- You need to know exact limits of public right-of-way so you can take appropriate measures in protecting existing roadways, shoulders, and the environment.

Rest assured that if your project's traffic or construction activity is viewed as causing damage within public right-of-way, you and your neighbors can be held liable for damages which may include costs to repair items such as pavement, subgrade, striping, curbs, landscaping, aprons, and cleaning out storm facilities.

Your first line of defense is to document pre-construction existing municipal conditions. Video the entire public right-of-way before you begin hauling or construction. Your second line of defense is to control your contractor.

When videotaping, include as much of the public road right-of-way as necessary. I recommend covering at least a half-mile beyond your limits of work. You can use your own camera and narrate as you go, or, better yet, hire a specialist. Produce a clean, accurate, and all-encompassing video. Consider it money well invested. If you do it by yourself, be sure to do it with someone who can help you pinpoint pre-existing damage as well as look out for traffic. As always, try to video after it rains and store the video in a safe deposit box.

➤ If you need a professional consultant, don't fight it. Hire one.

It is easy to put off seeking professional advice during the roadway planning and construction process especially when considering the money saved. It is also very easy to exceed "Dad's ability."

Construction mistakes and reconstruction are extremely expensive. Wasting other people's money doesn't go unnoticed.

Landowners who get in "over their heads" usually end up seeking professional advice somewhere along the line. They call either an engineer or contractor to bail them out. By the time they hit this stage, costs mount and schedules are usually blown. Rather than spending your way out of problems through trial and error, seek professional advice and guidance at your first impulse that you should do so.

In general, some examples of potential construction items that should not be attempted without input from an experienced professional include:

- Logging.
- Hard-paved surfacing.
- Large road cuts and fills.
- Blasting and demolition.
- Working in active traffic.
- Grading or work on steep slopes.
- Storm pond and water detention work.
- Retaining walls, bridges, and shoring work.
- Loading and hauling boulders and large rock.

- Utility work in and around any existing utility lines.
- Installing pipe systems greater than 18 inches (450 mm) in diameter.

➤ Only consider traditional "cold asphalt patch" for what it was intended for—temporary patchwork.

Unlike today's well-designed cold asphalt mixes, traditional cold asphalt patch material isn't adequate for permanent hard-surface repairs. It fails to bond and seal against existing pavement and eventually separates, degrading with traffic. Given time, temporary cold patch asphalt will compact below the surface of your road. Water can settle into these dips and leak through to the soil's subgrade as shown in Figure 7-1.

Temporary solutions rarely imply cutting. Instead, the temporary patch is

Figure 7-1. Water infiltration at an asphalt patch.

Figure 7-2. A cracked and lonely asphalt patch surrounded in a sea of failure.

filled into a ragged, uneven hole as defined by the limits of original failure. Gaining full adhesion and surface-to-surface support is almost impossible. Consider temporary patches the way you would a temporary dental crown—with utmost caution.

Likewise, when repairing asphalt potholes with concrete, concrete plugs do not flex over time, as adjacent asphalt will. This results in hard bumps, rising "whiteheads," and eventual loosening of the concrete plug. Concrete plugs also act as wedges during dry weather. They get pushed down with traffic loading. With wet and freezing weather, frost heave pushes these plugs above the surface of the roadway, impeding the road surface.

Once water permeates the hole and surrounds the plug, nothing remains to prevent the subgrade soil from saturating again. Softening soil and an inflexible moving wedge can work to create a larger pothole than the original plug was meant to fill.

Incidentally, naturally occurring, rounded rocks act in the same manner. They rise in the winter due to freezing soil conditions, slowly thrusting upward toward and above the road's surface.

Temporary measures are meant to get you through to a permanent fix later, although, as witnessed in Figure 7-2, sometimes the permanent fix never comes. A better solution is to fix asphalt pavement failures once and correctly with either hot mix or specially designed cold mix asphalt—not cold patch.

➤ Avoid other temporary "money sinks."

Road restoration based on good intent and poor advice will cost you a bundle of money. Don't throw new money after old and established problems. You have to ask yourself, "did last year's roadwork money result in permanently fixing anything?" Before cracking the checkbook again, wait until you can do the job correctly. Save yourself time, money, and heartache by abstaining from the following practices and rallying cries:

- **"Grading it should fix it."** Without addressing the road's deeper problems, surface grading only provides temporary relief.

- **"We'll use whatever material we have to fill potholes."** More of the same means more trouble later.

- **"More rock will save us."** Those who ignore or who are too mentally lazy to follow proper construction methods and sequencing tend to throw an annual "rock" budget at roadways. Flee from those who automatically proclaim, "more rock." More rock is rarely the answer. You can and will forever pour rock into a poorly built roadway. Year after year, dirt roads gobble up rock indiscriminately thrown onto them. Rounded rock disappears quicker than crushed rock. Buy once and buy right.

- **"Just rock the road, our cars will pack it down."** Unless structural material or rock is compacted and rolled into the road, your surfacing will not last long. Traffic will churn it, kick it, and roll it into ditches or off windshields.

*Figure 7-3. Multiple poor asphalt patches, lack
of curve widening, and transverse cracks.*

- **"Are you crazy? Cut the pavement to fill it?"** Don't
  follow the example shown in Figure 7-3. Refrain from
  filling asphalt or concrete pavement to ragged and broken
  edges. Instead, sawcut edges, repair, and treat the joints.

➤ Guard against loss of records.

Keep all documentation, plans, designs, and receipts in a safe place.
Distributing copies of this information to neighbors, consultants, and
contractors will also help to keep multiple copies available somewhere.
Organize and develop "job folders" as working documents for each and
every project that you and your neighbors undertake.

The "job folder" should contain the following:

- Daily diaries.
- Copies of photos and videos.

- Copies of permits and other legal papers.

- Receipts for all materials purchased and equipment rented.

- Copies of all communications between neighbors, including meeting minutes.

- A copy of the approved plans, bid documents, consultant reports, and specifications.

- Records of neighbor involvement. Note who did what and when. Include the number of hours worked.

- A full set of updated plans including all changes and any "as-built" information. "As-builts" are measurements of what was actually constructed.

- A candid but comprehensive accounting of surprises and unknowns that were encountered during construction. Include copies of any and all change orders resulting from these unexpected surprises.

- A copy of the contractor's contract including scope of work, exclusions, and any related documents. Compare the contract cost before and after completing work. Document any cost variances, issues, and conditions while things are still clear in your mind.

- A list of the contractor's equipment, approximate number of hours used, time of daily work, daily weather, and number of personnel. Include copies of any directives issued to your contractors.

- A full accounting of all monies submitted by whom as well as a cost summary including remaining association funds.

Proper recordkeeping will allow you easy access to needed information in the event that you need warranty information, project history, or to research items in dispute.

➤ Have an accurate cost estimate.

If you or your neighbors are not capable of building a cost estimate, you can hire any number of professionals who would be happy to formulate a reliable construction cost estimate for you. Such professionals may include construction consultants, civil engineers, or road construction contractors.

Once your initial cost estimate is in hand, do not forget to include the contractor's profit and risk, state and local taxes, permit fees, and a contingency value.

Contingencies usually range from 15 percent on high risk projects to a low of 5 percent after most unknowns disappear. I would not recommend a contingency value lower than 5 percent for any road construction budget, nor at any time during a project's schedule, short of total completion. Things happen and you need to be covered. However, it may be prudent to budget a contingency greater than 15% when your project exhibits an unusually high degree of uncertainty for any phase of work.

Examples of potential high risk factors include:

- Unknown subsurface soil, rock, and water conditions.
- Covering the cost of neighbors who will not share in expenses.
- Unforeseen weather and unseasonable or harsh climatic conditions.
- Factors related to extra work including overtime, additional equipment, and materials.
- Onerous requirements related to permit applications such as environmental restrictions, tighter specifications, and fees.

Contingency factors are also affected by the size of your project, total dollars, and the probability of modifying the contractor's scope of work as your project progresses. Seek professional advice when adding contingency value into your cost estimate.

If you solicit cost estimates from various contractors for budget purposes only, it is good practice to offer to pay them for their time. Even if you plan on hiring one of the contractors later to perform the work, paying them for their time and input now will absolve you from obligations whether actual or implied. Paying for advice and professional assistance is just good business.

Be sure to meet in the field with any professional whom you are considering hiring to build your cost estimate. This will give you an opportunity to ask questions and learn from a field perspective, what type of individual(s) you are dealing with. An onsite field meeting will also allow you to learn more about his or her approach to construction methods while allowing you to evaluate his or her style. You'll also learn a great deal about road construction and what you're getting into.

If you are working without a permit, a civil engineer or construction consultant can be hired on a regular basis, or at least retained on-demand, in order to help inspect or provide management services. This third party influence can help to blunt any short cuts that a contractor may contemplate while facilitating problem-solving along the way.

Danger exists when a contractor gives a sweet, low number that proves to be inadequate for the job. A contractor may not perceive you and your neighbors as repeat customers or he may just be positioning himself to walk into your job and later, submit deep charges for extra work and changes. In some instances, such extra work may have never happened or it was really part of the original scope of work. But when you are being tested, things can get real nasty, real quick. Such opportunists can be smoked out early enough but only with experienced help.

Be prepared and be forewarned. Hire expertise if you and your neighbors lack the experience and knowledge to manage your road restoration project.

➤ A word about tons, cubic yards, and more cubic yards.

One item worth mentioning concerns materials that are delivered and billed by weighed units such as tons. Weighed products usually come from pits with certified weigh scales or by trucks that have on-board scales. This material is almost always more expensive than "street available" fill material that originates from a source other than a commercial pit.

If you purchase rock or dirt and it does not come pre-weighed, and you do not have a method of weighing the product, you will probably be billed by the "cubic yard." The term "cubic yard" (cubic meter) means many things to many people and it's one of the most misunderstood elements in the construction industry, let alone, in sitework.

A dump truck's box capacity at struck level governs basic truck cubic yard measurement. Struck level is the square volume any truck box holds if the load fills the box completely flat and remains no higher than the top of the box not including added sideboards or box modifications.

Almost always, a truck cannot legally haul an equal capacity of rock or dirt that it boasts in struck box capacity. The reason is this: highway weight restrictions severely limit haul capacity. That means, trucks can max-out in weight *before* they do in box capacity. When you purchase unweighed materials by dump truck, you may be billed per struck box capacity (also called truck cubic yard) and not by what was *actually hauled in bank cubic yard volume.* So ultimately, it takes more truckloads to get what you want, and you may end up paying more than you thought you would for the same delivered volume, because, you're really paying by weight disguised as volume. You may also view this as an increase in unit price per delivered cubic yard of material.

But wait, there's more—and it's not all bad. Cheaper and very usable dirt or rock material may be available from an excavation somewhere where scales are not present, yet the material is "dirt-cheap" to coin a phrase. Paying more per unit is always a deal if it's still the cheapest unit in town, but it can get downright confusing.

Contractors who control local job site excavations may be hauling to a dump where they have to pay a dump fee. By selling you this dirt cheaply instead of dumping it, both parties win. The contractor saves dump fees and makes a profit. You save big dollars by purchasing quality excavated material that is cheap enough by the truck cubic yard to cover the volume underage resulting from being billed according to the truck's rated box capacity.

To be sure, when estimating cubic yardage, material volumes, and rock quantities, consider hiring a professional or a very good and trustworthy contractor.

Typical Budget Busters

During road construction, some activities are statistically more likely than others to cost more than expected. Somewhat predictable or common extra cost items vary according to project, region, and weather. More precisely, if extra costs do occur, they're most likely attributed to:

- Poor and unseasonal wet weather.

- Price inflation of construction materials.

- An unanticipated increase in poor soils, stumps, and subsurface water.

- Increased lineal footages of pipe, culvert, and fabric beyond those quantities as planned.

- Last-minute professional survey and layout requirements or the need for unanticipated geotechnical (soils and paving) consulting.

- Changes in scope of work or added "goodies" such as having a neighbor request additional ditching, driveway work, or retaining walls not included in the original budget.

- Lack of neighborhood cooperation. A breakdown in neighbor participation and volunteer labor results in everyone paying more to accomplish the same work.

- The unanticipated cost of potholing. This means digging and filling lots of smaller holes to uncover and confirm the existence and location of underground utility lines, subsurface water, buried debris, and soil type before commencing with construction.

- Unknown permit or application fees.

What Else Can We Do to Save Money?

Here are some money-saving guidelines:

• **Avoid buying more crushed rock than necessary.**

• **Estimate accurately and do not over-purchase.** Once you know your required rock quantities, purchase no more than 5 percent above the quantity you need. If you need more, purchase only what you need.

• **Gradually add crushed rock in increments over time.** When the lowest layer of rock is properly installed, add to it each year or seasonally until no further rock is needed. The final quantity of rock depends on your budget and targeted roadway standard. This method allows you to spread your cumulative investment in rock over a number of years while affording you the benefit of still running on it. Test it. Look for weak spots. You can purchase layers of rock as you can afford or only purchase enough for spot repairs.

• **Be opportunistic.** Shop around. Depending upon your region, rock prices can vary significantly depending on size and availability. Keep in touch with pits and contractors. Let them know what type of rock you're interested in purchasing and at what price. Systematically layering rock according to availability lowers your rock purchasing costs since you're only importing it when it's in over-supply or liable to be discounted by suppliers.

• **Buy less and preserve what you buy.** One way to accomplish this is by using engineered fabric and grid over larger areas of poor soil subgrade in lieu of massive amounts of larger rock. Fabrics and grids effectively separate rock layers from soil subgrade. This separation is crucial to keeping your rock working as road base and not being swallowed up by deeper, unstable subgrade soils. Wet, organic, and uncompacted soils slowly displace rock with native subgrade soils. Over time, your rock disappears and the road surface reverts back to its native dirt condition. Then as the dust flies, you wonder, "Where did our rock go? Who took it?"

➤ Avoid contractor mark-up where possible.

Let's begin this topic by saying that you need to be fair with your contractors. They are more than entitled to make a fair and equitable profit on their labor, equipment, and material purchases.

Landowners, however, do have the option to purchase materials such as fabric, grid, culverts, rock, asphalt, and concrete directly from suppliers. With the right contractor, this approach shouldn't be an issue. What becomes an issue is liability. Self-purchasing materials shifts the burden to you and your neighbors to purchase the correct materials, in accurate quantities, and in a timely fashion. You may also gain liability for taking safe delivery, providing storage, and for placing ordered items where the contractor wants them, when he wants them.

It's often said that only contractors get a *contractor discount* but many suppliers will work with you if you have:

- Cash on hand.
- A friend in the business.
- A need for their expertise.
- A "no-fooling" present need.
- Sufficiently large quantities of material to order.
- A means for loading and transporting materials from the supplier's yard.
- A project that can help the supplier gain some degree of civic duty, advertising, or exposure.

Landowners can save additional mark-up by directly contracting with all consultants and surveyors. In other words, the landowner becomes the general contractor and construction manager. Again, you incur a degree of liability but if saving money is important to you, find a way to get involved now, and, later, enjoy your "sweat-equity."

➤ Avoid constructing more road width than absolutely necessary.

Refer to Figure 7-4. You *can* survive by only upgrading one running lane down the middle of your road. You'll still need room to pass but that can happen on shoulders or at turnouts. In order to accommodate a wide range of vehicles, the minimum center strip road width should be no less than eleven feet (335 cm) and it can be built up with crushed rock or hard surfaced.

If you choose to build a quality crushed rock center roadway strip, shoulders and adjoining areas such as turnouts, crossroad intersections, and driveways should be graded with the finest material that you can afford and they must match the elevation of your center travel lane.

Figure 7-4. A center-of-the-road, single lane asphalt paving job.

If you choose hard surfacing for the road center lane, it's even more critical that you match elevations between paved and non-paved road areas. Observe the elevation differences between paving and shoulder as portrayed in Figure 7-5. It's also important that you construct these non-paved road areas correctly to ensure that they don't settle or pothole. After all, you'll want to protect new pavement from vehicles jumping onto or diving off of the road's hard edge. Such edge wear causes hard surfacing to crack, chip, and break away.

The keys to making a narrow centerline ribbon of gravel or hard surfacing work effectively depends upon the following:

- Minimum center road width should be no less than eleven feet (335 cm).

- Shoulders, driveways, intersections, and turnouts should still be adequately constructed to receive vehicle loading and travel.

- Provide ample opportunity for vehicles to pass each other by providing either shoulders or turnouts at *equal elevation* to the center running lane.

Figure 7-5. Elevation differences between pavement and shoulder.

- Attaining proper drainage can be more complicated with multiple adjacent road sections. Be sure that the center strip and side sections work as a unit, smooth and with continuous grade.

➤ Keep excavated material dry.

If you plan on using road and trench dirt for structural fill purposes, it must be protected and kept dry. This is accomplished by piling the material into the smallest footprint possible, rolling or compacting it as it gets piled, and covering it with plastic during the evening hours.

Rolling the pile reduces ruts, creases, and loose surfacing prevalent with stockpiled dirt. A tighter, smooth surface results in less overall area for collecting and holding moisture. During the day, if it's not raining, *remove* any plastic and expose the pile to wind and sunlight. Evening coverage helps protect stockpiles from fog, dew, and unexpected midnight rain but plastic also prevents the moisture from condensation to escape through evaporation. During periods of construction inactivity, stockpiles should be covered and protected. In the end, depending upon your location and type of soils, use your best judgment when protecting stockpiled material.

➤ Require all individuals to pay according to use.

Review the payment options listed in Chapter 6 and decide what works best for you and your neighbors. Obviously, the more financial support you receive, the more you can do and the least it costs everybody.

Improving Your Odds of Doing it Right the First Time

Begin by knowing what your neighbors want. What do you want? What does the road need? Do they jibe?

Once you know what you want, and depending on how much you plan on doing yourself, clearly communicate the plan to your neighbors, and, if known, your consultants and contractors. Hire consultants and contractors only after interviewing them with your core group. There is no turning back if you choose the wrong consultants or contractors. If a neighbor is involved in the construction industry, that person may have contacts with able and trustworthy contractors. Otherwise, trade associations and material suppliers remain good places to find reputable contractors. A properly executed contract will also help to ensure smooth sailing to job closeout.

➤ Plan for the snowplows.

If your roadway routinely gets snowed-under, don't leave anything that could be wiped out later by a snowplow. Snowplows aren't delicate creatures. They indiscriminately shave everything in their path. So try to save above ground appurtenances and decorations such as reflective markers, rocks, sprinkler heads, lighting, mailboxes, and fences from the perils of plowing by locating them as far from the edge of the roadway as possible. Snow load may also cause landscaping and small trees to distort and blend into the landscape. Be sure to place supple and low-lying vegetation far enough away from the road's edge to avoid being driven over or crushed by plowed snow.

In snow country, plan for and provide snow storage areas along roadways. Plowed snow has to go somewhere and when it melts, any investment in sand and gravel will be easier to collect for reuse.

Unsurfaced gravel roads will inadvertently have an amount of gravel and dirt surfacing scraped to the road's edge, or onto your lawn, during plowing. This harms subgrade by opening and exposing fresh soil and gravel to both traffic and weather while creating a springtime chore in requiring you to regrade these deposits back onto the roadway. Hard surfacing eliminates this nuisance.

Another protective measure includes earmarking fences, ditchlines, hydrants, culvert ends, and landscaping with above-ground markers. While working in a world of white, snowplow operators can't differentiate much without some form of colored reference or warning. For this purpose, use bamboo poles or PVC pipe painted with bright orange spray paint. Hang a colored flag on each pole at least two feet higher than the highest level of snow that you'll ever expect to cope with.

In advance, provide your snowplow operator with a sketch that details roadside appurtenances, features, fences, and landscaping. Give it your best shot. Although damage-free snowplowing may be a myth, at least you can help minimize your pain when springtime arrives.

➤ Plan for fire trucks and moving vans.

Meet the criteria for these vehicles and your road will be able to handle just about anything.

Don't miss the chance to ensure for fire truck access. National fire code requirements are gradually being applied in regulating private roads. Although implementation isn't yet universal and, in truth, some private roads are terminally too steep, narrow, or restricted to meet fire code without incurring cost-prohibitive modifications, every effort should be made to accommodate fire trucks and emergency vehicles. Generally, the Uniform Fire Code requires:

- An all-weather surface. In other words, weather and road conditions would not prohibit fire truck access. Many fire trucks have clearance limits of six inches to eight inches between the bottom of the truck and top-of-road surface. Any dips or humps in the roadway that result in less clearance underneath fire trucks can cause the trucks to get "hung-up" and possibly even prevent them from responding in an emergency. In addition, in order to accommodate fire and larger truck tractive requirements, unimproved gravel roads may have to be built flatter in grade than surfaced roads. Minimum curve criteria (see below) and hard road surfacing become issues when guaranteeing all-weather access.

- A minimum 20 feet (610 cm) width of clear lateral driving surface.

- A turn around (cul-de-sac) on dead end roads sufficient in geometry to accommodate fire trucks.

It's good practice to contact your local fire department and ask what the current and future requirements may be. This also affords you an opportunity to provide information on improvements and changes happening on your roadway.

At minimum, your road and driveway should be at least 12 feet (365 cm) wide to allow trucks enough lateral (mirror to mirror) room for one-way access. Most large truck and trailer rigs also require minimum road curve geometry that helps prevent trailers from climbing into the roadway ditch, over-dale, and into your new split-cedar fence. Consult a local civil engineer about this issue if you think that you may have some tight roadway curves issues. Curve problems are prevalent in hilly terrain and where roads have been established firm to property and section lines. Examples of insufficient curve width and subsequent road damage from wandering tires can be seen in Figures 2-3 and 7-3.

➤ Get rid of subgrade moisture before construction.

Install "French drains" and ditch roadways the year *before* you plan on doing construction. Focus on "through cuts" and road sections where the surrounding ground is at the same or higher elevation than your road's surface. Figure 7-6, French drain systems, illustrates how and where drainage systems can be applied along a roadway.

By definition, a through cut is an area where the road has been cut through a hill or knob. You can tell that you are in a through cut if there is an embankment or slope climbing *up* from each side of the road. If your roadway has through cuts, the chances are you are *forever* suffering from potholes in these areas. That is because subsurface water drains down and out of the through cut from underground sources and into your roadway. Overland water also flows down from through cuts and onto the road. The road never gets a chance to "breathe." Continual water softens the road year-round. When driven upon, potholes emerge.

French drains and ditches, if installed the year prior to work, will help give the subgrade a chance to dry out. The soils will have a better chance of being suitable for construction. Otherwise, these soils would probably

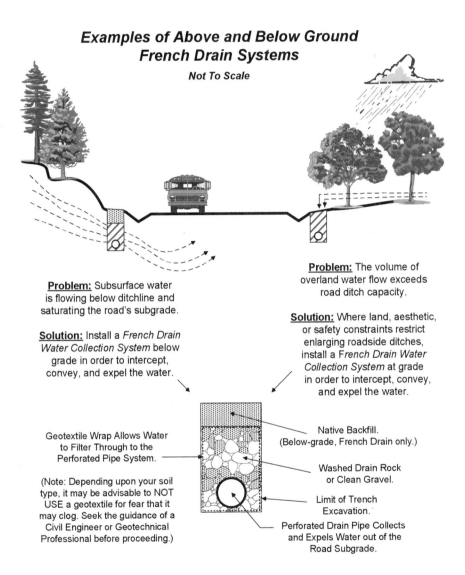

Examples of Above and Below Ground French Drain Systems

Not To Scale

Problem: Subsurface water is flowing below ditchline and saturating the road's subgrade.

Solution: Install a *French Drain Water Collection System* below grade in order to intercept, convey, and expel the water.

Problem: The volume of overland water flow exceeds road ditch capacity.

Solution: Where land, aesthetic, or safety constraints restrict enlarging roadside ditches, install a *French Drain Water Collection System* at grade in order to intercept, convey, and expel the water.

Geotextile Wrap Allows Water to Filter Through to the Perforated Pipe System.

(Note: Depending upon your soil type, it may be advisable to NOT USE a geotextile for fear that it may clog. Seek the guidance of a Civil Engineer or Geotechnical Professional before proceeding.)

Native Backfill.
(Below-grade, French Drain only.)

Washed Drain Rock or Clean Gravel.

Limit of Trench Excavation.

Perforated Drain Pipe Collects and Expels Water out of the Road Subgrade.

Figure 7-6. French drain systems.

have to be unnecessarily removed and replaced with dry imported material, bought and delivered from a gravel pit.

➤ Do not perform road restoration during wet weather.

Why invite trouble? Unless you have an emergency or absolutely no choice, do not perform road excavation, grading, or trenching during wet weather.

Rain and moisture can turn marginally good soil into unusable mud. In roadways, muddy material must be replaced with dry and compactable material. Costs escalate when you haul in and dump bad material and then haul in better soil to take its place. Review Figure 7-7 for some alternatives in dealing with wet and weak subgrade.

If you must perform roadway grading under wet conditions, consider the ambient temperature and wind conditions. They directly affect how quickly the ground will dry out while it is being worked.

As temperature decreases, it takes longer for the ground to dry out. The temperature variable begins to work in reverse below freezing since frozen conditions help to drive moisture out of most soils. Frozen and cold conditions present another portfolio of trouble, but contractors accustomed to northern climates may be able to cope and succeed without difficulty in completing your job—provided you're not placing concrete or asphalt. Although somewhat less prone to moisture problems, frozen soils do not grade easily. The worst scenario for working wet soils occurs just above freezing.

Windy conditions can help dry the ground and subgrade. The warmer the wind, the more moisture it can hold. Warm dry winds pick moisture out of open soil and carry it away.

On balance, limit roadwork to dry weather conditions. It's cheaper, safer, and cleaner.

Alternatives For Stabilizing Weak and Wet Subgrade

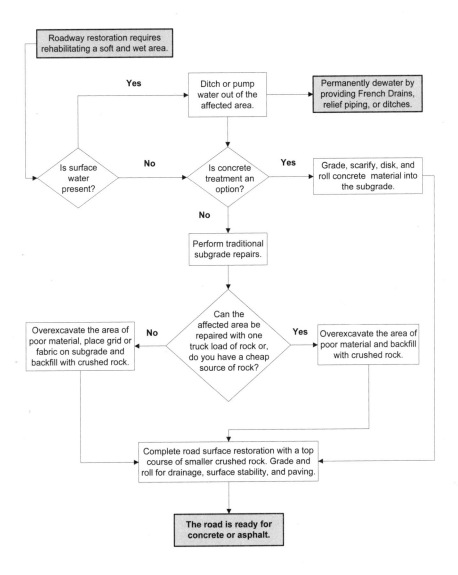

Figure 7-7.

➤ Do not skimp on geotextile fabric or grid.

An investment in geotextile grids and fabrics is well worth the cost. The people who sell and distribute these materials usually offer free engineering expertise and savvy advise. Many distributors can recommend competent contractors and will help beyond the scope of just selling you materials.

Being so inexpensive relative to the cost of grading, surfacing, and rock, geotextiles are worth adding solely for redundant structural reasons. As a backup component of your restoration work, geotextiles provide an extra measure helping to guarantee roadway performance and longevity. Think of it as additional insurance.

Just remember that geotextiles should go in before adding any rock or pit-run material to an open excavation or graded subgrade. They also go down before paving and surfacing depending upon your roadway restoration objective or standard.

➤ Plan to pay for some survey control and as-builts.

This is not the place to save money. It's important to know the limits and location of your road relative to its easement or right-of-way. This ensures that the road and repairs are, in fact, contained within and owned, or legally controlled, by the landowners who are performing the work. Private property rights and limits of ownership must be respected.

Also, don't make the mistake of underestimating your need for adequate survey or alignment control. Flat ground can be deceptive. Water may flow in a direction contrary to what your eye suggests as grade. Culverts suffering from reverse slope or that sag can harm subgrade more than having no pipe installed at all. Volumes of water forever sitting on pipe joints can eventually work into the subgrade. This is especially true if the pipe were to settle or develop lack of lateral support due to insufficient backfilling.

If you do not have seasoned equipment operators on hand who are able to read the ground without control or staking, some staking or grade control must be established. Misgrading and erroneous culvert installation can lead to added repairs, lost time, and increased cost. Follow the old adage: measure twice and cut once!

You should also plan on paying the surveyor to measure and chart exactly what you've installed and where it is. If you feel confident in your ability to measure and record, perform the as-built documentation yourself. Whatever you decide concerning as-builts, take lots of photos. Video the process and always capture something in the background that provides a reference when reviewing your subject matter later.

➤ Plan well in advance.

• **Plan the work.** Avoid changes to the plan once construction is underway. Think about changes made during road construction on par with changes made during home remodeling. It's not good practice unless you like reaching for the wallet. Once underway, changes come at a premium and, on small jobs, the contractor may not welcome such changes.

By keeping to your plan, you first save the additional cost of coordination. Second, you save the cost of tearing out new work. Third, you save the stress involved in making the changes, haggling with contractors, and prolonging the schedule. Plan all work thoroughly, and stick to the plan.

• **Comply with environmental standards**. When performing road construction and maintenance activity, you must comply with all standards set forth by federal, state, and local environmental regulations. At minimum, this applies to erosion control, preserving clean air and water, sensitive area regulations, construction material selection, and chemical applications.

• **Renting?** Are you going to rent equipment? If so, be sure to give the rental outfit plenty of notice for what you want and when you want it. Show up on time to pick up any rented equipment and return it to the rental yard on time. Plan enough time to fuel and clean rented equipment.

• **Purchase enough materials.** I have found it wise to always plan for the worst, and order the maximum quantities of everything that you *could* need. Naturally, this has limits but do you get the point? After all, as long as materials are not damaged, most supply houses will accept homeowner returns with a cost for trucking and, possibly, a restocking fee. If your plans include picking up pit materials, get there on time. On weekends, even the guy running the local pit wants to go home early.

It is also good practice to strategically stockpile all materials that you will need days before working. If there is enough room, pipe may be strung out adjacent to the alignment where it will be placed. Imported rock and pit-run can be stockpiled and covered.

If you find early enough in the construction process that you have over ordered materials or that you do not need everything that you have ordered, you can cancel ongoing deliveries by informing your supplier or trucker that you have enough. Just bring a halt to all pending deliveries.

• **Get in line, brother.** Order mixed materials that have a limited "shelf life" well in advance. Give all suppliers of manufactured "hot" products, including concrete and asphalt, plenty of time to schedule you in. The ideal time of year for targeting your construction happens to coincide with the busiest period for most batch plant operations. Everyone wants hot-mix products when the weather is right and it's during this time that the demand tests the supply. If your concrete or asphalt supplier must make a choice between delivering to you or to one of their regular clients or contractors, you will come in second every time.

• **Be ready for "hot" delivered materials.** The materials that cost the most tend to be manufactured items such as concrete and asphalt. Once they leave the plant, they are yours. Make sure your contractors are ready to accept and place whatever you order. Subgrades must be right, paving and screed machines must be ready, and survey control must be in. Act quickly once these products arrive. Returning such materials is virtually impossible.

• **Consider installing conduit for future wire and cable services.**
Strongly consider installing as much PVC conduit down your roadway as
possible in case a communication or cable utility company someday wants
to bring cable or fiber optic lines into your neighborhood. The road association will own this conduit and, once it's in place, to the right utility
purveyor it can be worth much more than what you paid to purchase and
install it. Sale or lease of this conduit to a communication or cable utility
company may more than offset the cost of the entire project and might
even pay to pave the road.

To be safe, install all conduit according to your local utility company
standards. Typically, conduit is installed no less than two feet (60 cm) deep
to a maximum depth of four feet (120 cm). Minimum allowable distances between certain utilities must be maintained. Depth depends upon
the utility. Your phone, cable, and power companies will supply you with
their construction and material requirements if you ask for them. They
will also flood you with specifications, procedures, and any other related
information pertinent to properly installing utility conduit. Make sure
that you have this information if you'll be dealing with dry utilities.

Communication and cable utility conduit is typically specified to be
minimum Schedule 40 PVC. Diameter should be no less than two inches
(50 mm) and can be as large as six inches (150 mm), although, for most
applications, four inches (100 mm) is most common.

Installing conduit for multiple utilities usually calls for laying plastic
pipe at varying depths and of different diameter. Once you've opened the
trench, the added cost of plastic conduit is relatively low but their alignments, your budget, and vault stubs must work or else you may be wasting money.

When installing dry utility systems, conduit should be stubbed into
and out of each lot or parcel along the route with a stout drawstring included within each pipe segment. Confer with your utility company
before planning for conduit installation. To your pleasant surprise, you
may find them in a check writing or "let's-make-a-deal" mood and
wouldn't that be nice!

• **Keep neighbors involved.** Call all neighbors weeks before starting work and inform them of the impending construction schedule. A few days before construction begins, take the time to remind all neighbors of their obligation and establish a meeting time and place.

Neighbors want the benefits of what you are doing. However, not everyone is willing to help physically or monetarily. This discomfort gets magnified if you choose to slowly restore the roadway over time. Although the end result is usually worth the hassles, projects involving people with varying incomes and expectations can leave you soul searching, and sometimes bitter. All the more reason to do it once—correctly—and get it over with.

Rules of Thumb and Painful Truths

Although every job is different, when planning roadwork, common sense is your ally. Remember the following truths when charting your course through road restoration:

• **Clear nights spell relief.** Cold weather can work for you since it helps to drive out subgrade moisture and sunshine usually follows such weather.

• **Speed and weight do the damage.** A speeding, lightweight vehicle can do as much damage to a roadway as a heavier and slower vehicle can.

• **"Mommy, that rock keeps getting bigger."** Freezing weather slowly drives large rocks to the surface of dirt roads. You can view some choice rising rocks in Figures 7-8 and 7-9. Emerging rocks slowly protrude and become apparent over time. Pluck them out when you can and mound the hole with crushed rock.

• **Picture this.** Take lots of photographs and video. Take pictures before construction commences, during construction, and after construction. Use this information to support contractor payments and to record what happened. Photos come in handy if legal and warranty issues arise later.

Figure 7-8. Rocks rising to the surface of an unimproved roadway.

Figure 7-9. More rising rocks.

Breeding Grounds for Road Failure

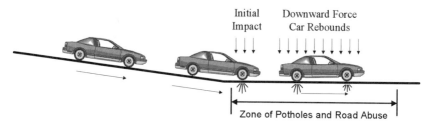

Vehicles traveling downhill bottom-out on flatter portions of a roadway
causing stress and potholes to develop within the road's surface.

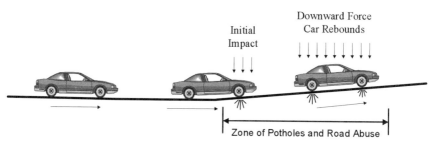

Vehicles suddenly thrust into an incline strike with force
resulting in stress, surface irregularities, and potholes.

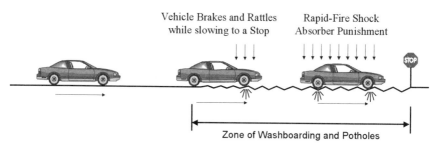

Fast moving vehicles that stop or accelerate too quickly on dirt
and gravel roads cause washboarding and potholes to occur.

Figure 7-10. Damages from vehicles braking and bottoming out.

Sharp Turning Vehicles Damage Roads

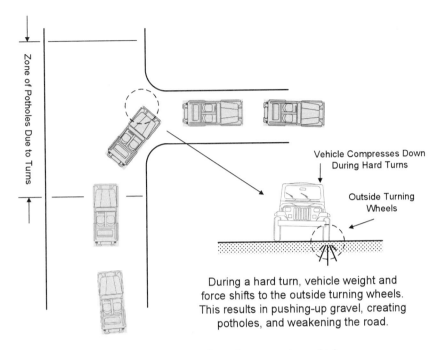

Figure 7-11. Damage from sharp-turning vehicles.

• **Sudden impact creates potholes.**Vehicles performing sharp turns and bottoming-out will accelerate roadway failure. Refer to Figures 7-10 and 7-11.

Potholes and cracked pavement are pronounced where driveway entrances and side roads join main roads. This is especially true where they join or cross at right angles. Sharply turned vehicles as shown in Figure 7-11 have their weight and inertia forced to the outside front wheels resulting in concentrated pressure along that tire's path. Repetitive wear and stress eventually causes failure.

One way to defer such damage is to slow down while turning hard in and out of driveways and crossroads. Permanent solutions involve overexcavating chronic areas of failure, treating the subgrade, and backfilling with structural material such as pit-run or crushed rock. Another technique involves cutting and grading such places flatter and into better alignment with the main roadway.

Areas where vehicles routinely bottom-out will fail. This occurs where driveways and side roads bottom-out onto a lower road or where an inordinate amount of braking occurs onto or off roadways.

The above conditions may require thicker sections of rock or hard surfacing in order to counter continual shock and pounding.

• **Dissimilar materials can lead to failures.** Harder materials in a roadway will cause abnormal and accelerated wear on adjacent softer materials. In other words, when exposed to vehicle traffic, softer materials will yield quicker than adjacent harder materials. Failures take place where dissimilar materials meet.

As mentioned earlier, avoid filling potholes on unimproved dirt roads with harder materials that set-up such as hot-mix asphalt or concrete.

• **All things being equal, relationships between dissimilar materials can be ranked as follows, in order:**

1. Wet soil yields to dry soil.

2. Loose dry soil yields to compacted dry soil.

3. Compacted dry soil yields to crushed rock.

4. Crushed rock surfacing yields to asphalt.

5. Asphalt yields to concrete.

6. Concrete yields to steel such as railroad tracks.

7. Everything eventually yields to large native boulders and exposed bedrock.

• **Common locations where roads fail due to dissimilar materials include:**

1. Railroad tracks and paved areas containing metal joints. Traffic pounding from a steel rail to a paved surface will eventually cause the adjacent paving (asphalt or concrete) to fail. Refer to Figure 7-12.

Under these conditions, asphalt will tend to cavitate and alligator whereas concrete will crack.

2. Dissimilar paving. Where traffic leaves concrete and lands on asphalt, asphalt will degrade. This is because asphalt gives and concrete doesn't, especially in warm weather. Beaten down asphalt in transition zones will depress and hold water developing "bird baths" and eventually fail. In addition, vehicles experience a bump or sharp lip when traveling from deformed asphalt to rigid concrete. Figure 7-13 shows a zone of massive asphalt damage where it transitions to concrete.

3. At bridges. Think of the bridges that you cross. Do you recall potholes and abrupt edges when driving over bridges such as the one shown on Figure 7-14? I know that I travel over plenty of bridges that have settling problems. Check for pavement repairs and continual road fills adjacent to the edges of bridges. This indicates that the bridge is settling at a different rate than the adjacent roadway. Being rigid structures, bridges

Figure 7-12. Damage to pavement abutting steel rails.

don't vertically flex equally with adjoining road movement. Reflective cracking and pavement failures flourish where bridge decking meets adjoining pavement. Said another way, concrete and steel are less forgiving than dirt and asphalt.

Other reasons for road problems adjacent to bridges include lack of proper fill and compaction during bridge installation and the fact that rain, water, and weather less affect a well-constructed concrete and steel bridge than they do the roads that cross them.

• Countering problems with dissimilar materials:

You can avoid problems with dissimilar materials by not mixing or installing differing products to do the same job. Instead, build with homogeneous materials and remove troublesome objects.

Figure 7-13. Damaged asphalt adjoining concrete.

Figure 7-14. Bridge settling and repairs.

Figure 7-15. If you have no choice but to deal with an existing condition, act to reinforce weak subgrades where dissimilar materials meet. Figure 7-15 shows multiple potholes where an unimproved road meets asphalt. With unimproved roads, excavate out poor and fatigued material, compact the subgrade, lay fabric and grid, and add adequate crushed rock. If your budget allows, overbuild these zones by going in once with additional materials and thicker surfacing. The only sure way to avoid such damage is to remove one material or mitigate the weaker material by bolstering it enough so that it can accept the punishment that it is taking. It never hurts to slow traffic either!

✓ More "Do's"

- Pothole before you dig.
- Use the One-Call System.
- Do it right and do it once.
- If in doubt, hire a professional.
- On complex projects, require survey control.
- Build a complete and comprehensive job folder.
- Know your physical, mental, and financial limitations.
- Avoid wet and cold weather when planning roadwork.
- Document everything with video, pictures, and diaries.
- Include future utility and conduit crossings when planning.
- Avoid the budget busters and money sinks listed in Chapter 7.
- Spend the time or money developing an accurate cost estimate.
- Identify and target subgrade issues where dissimilar materials meet.
- Study your project enough to know what equipment to rent or hire out.
- Save as much money as you can now; you can add improvements later.
- Culverts have to drain in the correct direction; there's just no other way.
- If you want to preserve and reuse the dirt that you excavate, keep it dry.
- Avoid providing a training ground for well-intentioned weekend warriors.
- Include fire truck, garbage truck, and moving van requirements in your planning.

- Purchase enough materials and schedule concrete and asphalt early in the process.
- Spend enough time figuring the right method in dividing costs between neighbors.
- Understand the principals of tonnage and cubic yards and how they can affect costs.
- Shop for your own contractor discount pricing; you may be surprised how much you save.

CHAPTER 8

Finding Help

Choosing the Right Contractor

Qualified contractors lead to quality construction. A capable contractor will save you time, money, and heartache while improving your odds of avoiding conflict and litigation. Remember, if you have a contractor or are planning to hire one as a consultant, get him into the process early. Competent contractors can help with cost estimating, material selection, grading options, and provide you with a warm, friendly feeling of partnership. See Figure 8-1, choosing a contractor.

If you plan on shopping your project amongst multiple contractors, build your contractor bid roster carefully. You can always bid or negotiate the work later with any of them depending on their pricing and enthusiasm for your job. When soliciting contractor information or building a prequalification list, your selection process should include the following checklist and observations:

- Does the contractor have a local business license?
- Does the contractor belong to the local Chamber of Commerce?
- Request and check the contractor's bank and financial references.
- Check the contractor's complaint history with the Better Business Bureau.

- Inquire about or request a list of the contractor's field and office manpower.

- Is the contractor licensed for business within your state? Is the license valid?

- What is the contractor's "in-house" policy on warranty and work guarantee?

- If the contractor is in a trade association or union, check these organizations for references.

- Request references from owners of completed work and from the contractor's main suppliers.

- Has the contractor ever filed for bankruptcy? Has he ever been sued? If so, when and why?

- Ask for copies of insurance certificates and verify coverage with your local labor and industry department. Do you need "hold harmless" and co-insurance for landowners? Ask your insurance agent about these options and what they mean to you and your project.

- What is the contractor's bonding status and capacity? Bonding companies scrutinize contractors before selling risk coverage to them. Although your driveway may not warrant issuance of a bond, information gathered from bonding companies can reveal much about your contractor's capability, experience, and reference.

- Request a list of or speak to the contractor about his equipment and resources. Is his equipment owned, leased or rented? Is he here to stay or will he be gone tomorrow?

- Request a list of key individuals who would be assigned to your project (superintendents, managers, foremen, schedulers, etc.). If your project is of sufficient size, ask for the resume of each person cited. Take the time to meet and speak with some of these people.

Choosing A Contractor

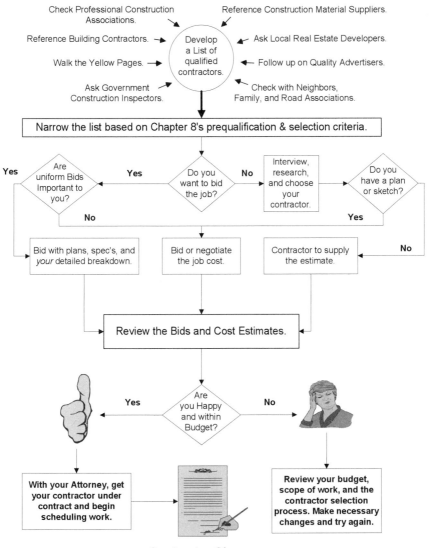

Check Professional Construction Associations.

Reference Construction Material Suppliers.

Reference Building Contractors. → Develop a List of qualified contractors. ← Ask Local Real Estate Developers.

Walk the Yellow Pages. → ← Follow up on Quality Advertisers.

Ask Government Construction Inspectors. → ← Check with Neighbors, Family, and Road Associations.

Narrow the list based on Chapter 8's prequalification & selection criteria.

Yes ← Are uniform Bids Important to you? ← **Yes** ← Do you want to bid the job? → **No** → Interview, research, and choose your contractor. → Do you have a plan or sketch?

No   **Yes**

Bid with plans, spec's, and *your* detailed breakdown.

Bid or negotiate the job cost.

Contractor to supply the estimate.   **No**

Review the Bids and Cost Estimates.

Yes ← Are you Happy and within Budget? → **No**

With your Attorney, get your contractor under contract and begin scheduling work.

Review your budget, scope of work, and the contractor selection process. Make necessary changes and try again.

Contractor Chosen

Figure 8-1. Choosing a contractor.

- Request a sample of the contractor's pay estimates. Are they complete, consistent and professional? Can you understand them? Will they stand as an adequate document of record?

- Visit some of the current contractor's worksites. Is the equipment well maintained? Is the equipment new? Is the equipment working, idle, or under repair? Are superintendent's pickups and flatbed trucks easily identified as belonging to the contractor? Are the work areas well maintained? Do the work areas appear safe? Are the work crews following both your state's and federal safety guidelines? Is anyone working?

- Request a list of projects completed to date. Visit these completed projects. What is your impression?

- How long has the contractor been in business? Under how many names has the contractor operated?

- Meet with the owner, estimator, and superintendent. Were they busy tending their mobile phones and pagers or were they intent on your meeting? Did they ask you pertinent questions? Did they seem to care?

- If the contractor has already bid your project, was the bid complete or was it glossed over and missing items? Did the contractor fill out your bid on "his" terms?

- If you need an environmental property evaluation, is the contractor qualified to perform a Phase 1 Assessment? Check the contractor's scope of insurance and environmental work history.

- An excellent source for contractor recommendations is the *municipality* in which you live or the agency which has issued your permits. Permit issuers and their inspectors may know of qualified companies experienced enough to get you built out. Follow the recommendations of your public inspectors. There is nothing quite like the path of least resistance!

- Has the contractor returned your calls and submitted all requested information expediently?
- Is this contractor qualified regardless of the price?

It's an exhaustive list but it gives you an idea of how a contractor can be evaluated. The magnitude and dollar value of your project will help dictate the level of detail you need in scrutinizing prospective contractors. Listen to the opinions of your neighbors and consultants. Also, trust your intuition. If something feels bad, it probably is bad.

If the references check out and the numbers add up and if it appears ready and able, is it still the right contractor? Ask any prospective contractor to produce the following information and numbers:

1. Tax revenue numbers.
2. A labor and industry number.
3. An employment security number.
4. Today's statement of bonding capacity.
5. A contractor license or business number.
6. Evidence of liability and workman's compensation insurance.
7. A list of the contractor's workers and phone numbers who will be on your job.
8. A statement or summary of potential cost saving ideas that the contractor can offer.
9. A cost estimate including a list to materials and quantities to be purchased. Attach this list to the plans or specifications for the job.
10. A linear bar schedule showing project duration, milestones,

and a breakdown of individual construction activities including start and finish dates.

11. Agree on the venue for arbitration or legal action should the need arise. Include a statement describing the conditions under which you or the contractor would be liable to pay penalties, damages, and legal costs.

➤ Some contractor preselection tips.

• **Be consistent**. Use the same evaluation for all subcontractors regardless of whether you or your contractor hire them.

• **Be formal.** For the record, collect all contractor responses in writing. Set a deadline for submitting bids and information and stick to it. Collecting this information in a timely fashion and requesting it in writing underscores your seriousness.

Do not ask for or proceed with verbal information. Instead, compose a uniform and complete bid format for all contractors to complete. Such packages make contractor comparisons easy later. Insist that contractors complete the bid packages as you've designed. Do not allow them to modify your bid. They should be able to add bid items that you've missed but under no circumstance should you accept their bid unless it's in alignment with your bid package. Discount contractors who do not respect or honor your procedures.

This process also "weeds out" uninterested, unorganized, or busy contractors. Better to know now, than later. Throughout the contract process, be sure to continue communication and decisions in writing. If something remains unclear or you require additional information, stop. Do not proceed until you fully understand the issue.

• **Be cool.** There is risk associated with examining your contractors this thoroughly. Sophisticated contractors may be insulted or frightened. If your project is small, they may feel that you're being too pushy. That you're not worth it. For sure, you can wear out your welcome. To counter this, use discretion with each contractor depending on how well your communication progresses. Shake and lose troublesome contractors as soon as possible.

• **Be fair.** If you don't plan on using a certain contractor to do the work but continue to seek his expertise and advice, pay him for his time. If you have a preferred contractor in mind but still want comparative cost figures, pay other contractors for their estimates. Share what you know with the contractor. Sometimes it's difficult to foresee exactly when work will begin or when permits will be issued. If you don' t know, tell him so. Do the best you can and be a team player. Clarity and tact go a long way to building a contractor's trust.

What About Construction Contracts and Bids?

➤ A lesson in wasting time and resources.

Unless you or someone in your association truly understands construction, civil engineering, and basic construction law, contracts and the bidding process should not be undertaken without professional guidance. It is amazing how many people think they understand the essence of road building, surveying, and civil engineering when they don't. Avoid neophytes of questionable scholar. They're worse than the weekend warrior and can cost you a bundle. People who persist in allowing road construction charlatans to spend their funds would be better off wadding the project's money into handfuls of $20 bills and flinging them into the crowded bleachers at a football game.

This is a serious issue. Unsuspecting and unknowing people all suffer when they follow misguided direction. I have seen it in its glory. The only antidote to this path of action is spending lots of money over and over again. Yes, it is possible; you *can* spend your way out of roadway problems. It takes years of trial and error, effort, and gnashing of teeth, but as the saying goes, throw enough at a wall and some will stick. The question is, how much money and time do you have to throw?

➤ Seek sage advice and experience.

There is a better way. When dealing with the bid and contract process, tap the experience, contacts, and knowledge of people in the road building profession. These people include the contractors themselves, consultants, attorneys, or any neighbors in these professions. Let them help guide the planning, design, and contractual issues.

Comprehensive and all-inclusive bids lead to good contracts! All succeeding documents build on the first document.

➤ Carefully consider your construction bid and work agreement strategy.

Construction pricing and bidding is a study unto itself, especially in sitework. For most private road construction projects, you can use any of the following formats for soliciting prices or bids. Which pricing strategy works best for your project? Which strategy suits your temperament? Carefully review the following contract, pricing, and bid strategies and then decide.

• Negotiated or bid lump sum pricing.

The lump sum method can work well for most road associations and private landowners. This method is clean, easy to administer, and the contractor's payments are straightforward and simple to understand. Basically, the contractor comes in, collects your bid package, bids the job, and, depending upon the size of the job, collects one full payment upon completion.

Generally, lump sum work agreements are not written against a unit-by-unit detailed list of work to be performed. Instead, with a broad brush, the deal is consummated with one price for the entire scope of work through job completion. Owners supply the plans and define the scope of work and schedule that contractors bid against. Contractors are comfortable with this method because it affords them great opportunity for profit. Private landowners like this method because it's not complex and they feel the risk gets shifted to the contractor with no increase in cost.

The positives: One payment can do it all. If work extends over a period of time, payments can be calculated based on percentage of work complete against the total contract amount. It's simple, easy to apply, and somewhat reduces your overall risk by shifting liability to the contractor for weather- and contractor-induced miscalculations. In other words, you're somewhat free from paying for problems that happen should circumstances evolve beyond your control or the control of your representatives. The contractor has incentive to finish work early.

The negatives: By the same token, if your road project includes many elements or phases of differing work, lump sum contracts may not do you justice. The reason is, the more complex the project, the more protective cost padding a contractor is apt to add since he will be bound by a "one price fits all work" scenario.

Lump sum deals are tough to evaluate if you have no idea which contractor left out what or how each contractor valued various aspects of the project. Without knowing your contractor's assumptions and cost elements, you have no base from which to develop fair pricing should charges be levied later in covering change order work. All you would know is how the contractor's bottom line price differs from his competitor's price. For you and your neighbors, the danger lies in getting less product than you bargained for, receiving lower quality work, or paying too much with minimal recourse.

Another negative involves your inability to accurately assign a dollar value for any work short of full completion. What happens if you dismiss your contractor or he pulls out early? How does he get compensated for work complete to date? You have no idea how to value segmented work to date because it's part of a one-price, lump sum scenario. Your contractor will have no problem billing for such work but can you trust his judgment, reasoning, and backup for a partial billing? You have little or nothing to gauge incomplete work against.

Landowners must still specify the rules of the bid such as scope of work, dimensions, and specifications. The more comprehensive the bid package, the better your odds are of not over-paying. With this method, landowners must remain engaged in the process. Lump sum is better suited for smaller and simpler jobs.

• **Contractor-driven lump sum pricing.**

This traditional noncompetitive pricing strategy involves receiving a lump sum, all-inclusive cost estimate as determined by *one* contractor. The contractor determines what he thinks you need to fix the road, then, by his own methods, the contractor measures and tallies the work to be performed. The cost you receive is totally on his terms. One number and it's all for you.

This faith-based approach is very simple to understand but it's tough to evaluate and can be doubly tough on the wallet. If the contractor is not competing against other contractors, your costs and schedule are completely in his hands with no point of reference.

The positives: This format is quick to execute and it's simple and easy to review. Everyone can understand it. If the price is affordable and fair, and you experience a minimal amount of changes during construction, it's a tough strategy to beat. In being clean and efficient, this approach works for people who don't want to get involved, or who have enough money to not care, or who have a contractor that is absolutely trustworthy and honest.

The negatives: It's one-shot, one contractor, and your money. Comparing contractor bids is non-existent. When problems occur, less information has a tendency to grate against trust especially when the contractor views you as a one-time client. Buyer beware.

Changes can turn into an expensive time and material exercise or worse yet, a cost overrun nightmare based on the contractor's interpretation of his or her own original costing. It's anybody's guess, and money is buried wherever the contractor chooses.

• **Lump sum based on unit pricing.**

Lump sum means that you pay the contractor a lump sum, bottom line amount. But, in this case, it's based on unit pricing. With this strategy, the contractor commits to (or bids) a series of basic unit prices for items such as installed lineal foot of pipe or truck cubic yards of roadway excavation to be removed. These unit prices are then multiplied against construction quantities in building the *lump sum contract*. A lump sum contract based on unit prices protects you in many ways.

The positives: This method works well for both budgeting and bidding purposes. When bidding, unit pricing allows you to compare all bids on equal footing, void of quantities. It provides a quick and easy vehicle for pricing change orders during construction. After all, it's not deviations in plan quantities that should dictate how you choose a contractor. Changes in quantities and scope of work happen regardless of whom you hire. Contractors should be chosen primarily due to pricing. Unit pricing allows you to corral your costs up front.

If and when you experience a change of conditions or if you want to add to or delete from the scope of work, pre-established unit pricing can be matched to quantity changes and be easily added to the contract. Lump sum strategy provides a contractor incentive to complete work early *and* to not get creative when billing.

The negatives: With this strategy you have to be sure that you're getting competitive unit pricing. You can get low unit pricing by negotiating with contractors or you can get it by collecting a wide range of unit prices through a bid process.

Unit pricing must be established early on to handle *any* construction activity that *could* possibly happen during construction and your unit pricing must be detailed. The more wide-ranging and detailed, the better. By covering all your bases, you leave a contractor less room to maneuver later should a change of conditions occur. Contractors who have had to competitively bid your work will almost assuredly reach for more profit if they perform change order work later that's not covered in your existing scope and unit price schedule.

In fact, contractors gain the upper hand when changes occur involving work that has not been already assigned a unit price. Without established pricing, the contractor is free to apply charges as he sees fit. You're at his mercy and your loss of control is further exacerbated if (break out the fiddle) construction changes occur during emergency conditions or poor weather.

This option allows you an opportunity to build an all-encompassing unit price schedule to which all work can be applied.

• Time and materials (T&M).

With time and material type contracts, you pay the contractor against actual invoices for materials, equipment, and manpower as documented in completing your job. The contractor's overhead, profit, and risk are buried in his hourly charges.

The positives: You pay according to what you get. The accounting can be complete, clean and phantom charges are not easily hidden. That is, provided someone documents work daily and knows exactly what transpired, when it happened, and what it took to accomplish the task.

Billings should match what you expect to pay and be easily justified according to the project plans and specifications. Time and material agreements work especially well if you can trust the contractor. They also work well if you have someone inspecting all work, validating equipment and operator hours, noting material deliveries and quantities, and recording any change of conditions.

The negatives: The contractor assumes minimal risk and no financial incentive to complete the project as quickly as possible. Unless a not-to-exceed clause is added to the contract, there is no ceiling to your cost liability.

Other exposure lies in the hourly rates. What contractor wants to, or is willing to, publish and only charge his in-house, bare-bones hourly rates. Unlike other pricing, T&M almost guarantees you'll pay equipment hourly rates more in line with market compatible "Blue Book" rates. What about personnel? If he charges you prevailing (union) scale, how do you know that he's actually paying his people accordingly? Materials are more forgiving as you'll actually see the invoices and pay for them plus markup for overhead and profit.

You may also pay for all change orders in full and usually at the highest conceivable market rate possible. To validate that you are not being overcharged on labor and equipment, someone must observe construction and document all activity. Time and material agreements can bring horrible results if you have a dishonest contractor or a contractor with no incentive to build cost-effectively or in a timely fashion. Costs can escalate quickly, extra materials may be erroneously purchased, and billable hours can easily get out of hand. If the contractor's paperwork is confusing, faint, or difficult to understand, your problems have only begun.

• Unit pricing. Measure and total it together:

Paying by the unit can be an attractive way to contract work. With this system, costing is tight, concise, and easy to administer. Items are costed per the lineal foot (meter), or square yard (square meter), or by some other measurable unit. In theory, you only pay for what you get. Everything is known and little can be hidden.

When squaring up with your contractor, you can arrange to pay against a lump-sum grand total based on unit pricing *or* grab a tape, and meet with your contractor to figure out the damages. I recommend the former approach as it takes less time and doesn't put you in a position to quarrel or exhibit ignorance should an argument ensue between you and the contractor concerning how quantities are measured or such.

The positives: This method works well for both cost estimating and paying for your work. Change order work that has already been assigned unit pricing is easy to control. You can direct your own destiny with unit pricing and most quantities are easily verified.

As an example, culvert installation would be paid for on a lineal foot (meter or cm) basis. No other cost or basis beyond total lineal feet could be billed toward installing the culvert. The same would happen with asphalt and concrete. Work would be paid according to final measured units such as by the square yard (square meter) or weighed delivered ton. Delivered dirt and rock can be paid for by the weighed ton, per truck cubic yard (truck cubic meter), or as graded and compacted in place by the finished square yard.

The negatives: It's hard to single out any negatives in using this strategy except that it takes expertise and planning to make unit pricing work. You need a detailed accounting of what work is going to happen as well as a list of what work could happen should conditions change. You also need accurate quantities if you care about budget. Afterall, when you're done pulling tape and agreeing on installed quantities, you don't need surprises. This may entail hiring a consultant who can build an accurate cost estimate and construct a quality bid package and pay schedule tailored to your advantage.

• **Cost plus.**

This strategy is similar to T&M in that you pay the contractor according to his actual costs plus an agreed upon overhead, risk, and profit fee. This charge is usually determined as a percentage of the base construction cost and gets tagged onto the pay estimate's grand total.

The positives: You pay the contractor according to his actual cost to complete the project. Overhead and profit are based on a known percentage and shouldn't be integrated into his hourly rates. The accounting can be clean and simple however, if the backup paperwork is shoddy or lacking, things can go sideways real quick. With this strategy, you need to clearly define what constitutes payable charges and establish a mechanism to review billings, hours billed, and to question any billing backup. Since the contractor's mark-up is calculated as a percentage of final base cost, focus your efforts on minimizing the base construction cost.

The negatives: The contractor assumes minimal risk and no financial incentive to complete the project as quickly or as cheaply as possible. If the contractor chooses a more costly construction method for completing work, you pay it. Unless a not-to-exceed clause is added to the contract, you will pay all change orders in full. Documentation remains critical to ensure that you are not paying for something that you do not receive.

Price strategies can also include any combination of the above methods. There are no hard and fast rules. How comfortable you feel with your contractor and your ability to safely negotiate a fair and reasonable contract may ultimately dictate which pricing strategy you employ. And that's what it's all about anyway.

➤ How do I go about formulating an effective bid that leads to a strong contract?

Begin by seeking the advice of those who have gone through a private road restoration project. Look into local road associations and other private road projects that have succeeded. What have they done? Consider bringing a contractor into the process early as an adviser and to possibly perform the work. A construction attorney or construction consultant may also have leads and information suitable to get you going.

If you must start from scratch, rely on locally qualified people to help formulate a custom bid. Don't rely on using a store-bought boilerplate bid outline or contract; they're useless. Most precooked, stock bid formats and contracts have been developed for structures, such as homes and commercial buildings. Structures are predictable and easily measured. Sitework cannot be "canned." It's too difficult to control and too variable in nature to predetermine. Avoid boilerplate sitework solutions.

Returned bids can be used as a vehicle to help test your estimate, budget, and scope of work. They'll indicate real costs for your project and aid in establishing a base for fair pricing. When bidding, include room on the form for contractors to add cost items that you may have overlooked. Use this information to perfect your contract or, later, build a more comprehensive bid package. However, if you rebid your project based on contractor input, remember to pay those contractors for their contributions and expertise.

As each region of the world has its own particular slant on contracts, weather, and what is or is not appropriate, contracts and bids must be tailored accordingly. Methods, standards, and cost vary widely. In addition, no two road restoration projects are the same. You can bet that no two road associations are the same.

Spend money on qualified counseling. Good advice is rarely free, and, it's true—you get what you pay for. If it costs you to gain qualified information and build strong bid and contract documents, spend the money and don't look back. You won't regret it later.

➤ When formulating and sending bids, consider the following checklist:

- Identify the plans, specifications, and documents that the bids are tied to. Note design dates, revision numbers, and number of pages within each set of bid documents.

- If you decide to pursue unit price bids, prepare the base unit schedule yourself. Do not rely on contractors to interpret the plans or offer their preferred unit breakdown. Use one consistent bid breakdown that will evenly apply to all bidders. This practice also helps minimize inaccurate estimating on behalf of your bidders.

- Will you be requesting each contractor to submit a detailed estimate? Have you budgeted money to pay for such contractor services if you end up later negotiating work with yet another contractor? If not, do so.

- How will change orders be priced? As mentioned above, it's good practice to get wide-ranging unit pricing in preparation for potential change orders.

- When work items are going to happen, yet it's not possible to price them at the time of bidding, establish an "in-house" allowance or contingency to draw from for completing this work. This in-house allowance should only be known to a select few and not by the contractor. Depending upon how well you've thought out your project and how well it's designed, contingencies commonly begin at approximately 12 percent and rise to whatever you're prepared to cover.

- Develop a clearly understood checklist of qualifications, licenses, and certifications that you expect to receive from each contractor.

- Depending upon your price strategy, tracking overhead, profit, and risk valuation may or may not be an issue. If your pricing strategy identifies these costs as line items, show them as such on the bid.

- Identify which materials you plan on purchasing and bid having them installed. On the bid, note that the materials on such and such line item are "owner provided." This strategy may smoke-out some higher pricing or a contractor who insists on doing everything. Some contractors may price buying *and* installing materials *cheaper* than what an owner can buy the same materials alone for. Contractor's that offer deep discounts or who discourage owner provided materials do so for many reasons, but it's usually done to get the job (lowest price), control the job, or get you out of the job. For those landowners who are about to go in over their heads, that may be a good thing.

- Unless your strategy is to utilize and finance prebidding so as to gather information and, later, compose a stronger bid, it's wise to bid only when you're prepared to begin work. Don't waste everyone's time before you're ready. You'll usually also attain the lowest pricing by bidding once since contractors tend to price work higher the second time around.

- Take your time and seek advice when preparing bids. Remember, entanglements concerning contractors and payments end up migrating to the weakest denominator, and, without proper planning and support, that could very well be you.

➤ **When receiving and reviewing bids, consider the following checklist:**

- Carefully review each contractor's exclusions, special stipulations, and general conditions. Compare them against each other and ask yourself, "Can I live with these?"

- Review each contractor's list of equipment, resources, and personnel as promised. Are they adequate? Is the equipment too big, too small, or just right?

- Can the contractor meet schedule? Are they including contingencies on completing your work? If so, be careful. You're looking for a clean, simple, and timely process. You don't want to start off under a set of conditions and you don't want to be put immediately on the defense.

- Review pricing but also review the condition of your returned bids. Are they beat-up and grease-stained or are they crisp and professional? Did you get what you requested in your format as specified? It's unlikely a contractor that doesn't care to impress you before signing the contract will try to impress you later, while under contract. In this case, judge the book by its cover.

- Be sure to acknowledge and thank all contractors that have responded to your query.

- Multiple bids in themselves do not reveal potential for contractor fraud. Using this checklist (and book for that matter) will go a long way toward helping you determine a contractor's character and reduce your risk of getting burned.

Remember that a quote is not a bid, and a bid is not a contract.

➤ **Critical issues concerning contract formulation include the following:**

• **Consult an attorney versed in construction law.**

• **Holding retained payments.** Retain a percentage of contract money owed the contractor until he has successfully completed the project and owes you nothing. Pay interest on the money with a smile. The contract should specify how retainage is held, accounted for, and specify under what conditions retainage can be released. Employ a reputable and solvent third-party entity such as an escrow company to hold retained funds. The amount of retainage held should not exceed those percentages common for roadwork in your area.

• **Payment method.** Depending on length of construction, how will the contractor be paid? A "draw schedule" will have to be agreed upon. This includes how, when, and where the contractor's pay requests will be submitted for compensation. How will the contractor be paid for purchasing materials on hand? That is, how will the contractor be paid for materials purchased and held, yet not installed? Or, will the contractor be paid according to milestones and completion dates? This item is usually dealt with when negotiating terms with the contractor.

Also include—and make no exceptions—that final payment shall be made to the contractor only after you know that:

• All liens are released.

• All subcontractors have been paid.

• All suppliers and rental companies have been paid.

• Any conditions related to construction permits have been met.

• All work has been completed, is satisfactory, and has been inspected and approved.

• **Construction schedule.** Is schedule important to you? If so, who'll be responsible for composing the initial schedule and who'll perform schedule updates? You (or your consultant) or the contractor? On schedule driven projects, do you want to impose penalties for failing to meet schedule? Grounds for such penalties must be clearly defined and included in your contract. Tie a copy of the schedule to your contract and understand how impacts related to weather, changes, and holidays can adversely affect your bottom line.

• **Disputes.** If a dispute between you and your contractor arises, by all means, avoid going to court. First, try talking. If that doesn't work, try it again. Exhaust your opportunities to work the problem out verbally. If needed, seek the insulation provided by a common and objective third-party entity such as a consultant or supplier. Get creative but avoid going to court. With an open mind, weigh the costs, benefits, and what's at stake.

If that fails, seek mediation. Mediation involves providing a trained third party to assist in facilitating communication. Although mediators don't rule one way or another, they help to find mutually acceptable solutions palatable to both parties.

If mediation fails, the next step is to seek an arbitrator who will hear both sides present their arguments and rule accordingly. In preparation for this possibility, clearly define in the contract the terms, conditions, and basis upon which arbitration can and will be pursued. In some cases, your local Better Business Bureau may assist in resolving contract disputes. Regardless of how you proceed, have an attorney review contractual language related to dispute resolution.

• **Inspection and quality assurance.** If you're not constructing under an approved permit that would include some form of inspection, how will you ensure the work is correct and complete? How concerned are you and your neighbors about quality? How can you measure quality if you aren't constructing to a set of designed plans and specifications? Who will work on your behalf, performing inspections and completing job-ending punchlists? Who officially says that the project is complete, you or the contractor?

These are tough questions but the answers lie in trusting somebody to protect you. It could be your contractor, someone you know who understands road construction, or a hired consultant. Every project is different but in all cases, you need quality assurance so make sure that you're covered.

It's also good practice to require that the contractor procure any required permits. Not you or your neighbor. This helps keep the contractor informed, involved, and committed.

• **Registration and certifications.** Tie contractor registration numbers, insurance certificates, licenses, and references to the contract. Make them one document.

• **Lien releases.** Nobody wants liability for someone else. Clearly spell out procedures, qualifications, and the time limit for your contractor *and* his suppliers to release liens and all property encumbrances.

• **Increased contractor scope of work.** How will extra work be dealt with? Who will authorize such work and under what mechanism and timing will added payments be made?

Begin by recognizing that construction entails a degree of risk. Are you comfortable with risk and have you set aside enough contingency funds for cost overruns?

One method of controlling costs for extra work involves setting dollar thresholds above which no change order work can proceed without prior, written approval. Afterall, your intent is not to impact or delay the contractor while he seeks direction. You want to him to proceed and complete the project as quickly and cheaply as possible. This little trick has a side benefit in that it forces the contractor to commit to pricing before pursuing change order work.

Take charge by finding out, beforehand, costs for extra work. Know your exposure before agreeing to it. Don't set yourself up for unwanted and surprise change orders that may cost more than you can imagine. Once extra work is performed, if you cannot afford it or you didn't want it, you're in trouble. If you agree to extra work and sign accordingly, it's all yours to pay for.

• **After-thoughts and complications.** If neighbors want the contractor to perform work on their property in conjunction with contracted project work, the conditions of liability, schedule, and payment allowing such work to proceed must be simple and clear. The last thing you need is a nonperforming contractor hiding behind perceived misdirection given by you, the association, or any neighbor requesting individual work. You also don't need mixed billings and duplicate charges. Ultimately, the best policy is to allow neighbors freedom to contract their own work, provided their work happens *after* your road project is completed and signed off.

• **List what you are promised.** In the contract, list whatever you have been promised in the bid and during contract negotiations. Identify personnel resources, equipment makes, machine models, and type of special attachments. Include when they will be on the job and when they will be absent. You don't normally need this hammer but it's nice to have it in the war chest should a battle ensue.

• **Who is in control?** Who will ultimately control the project, you or the contractor? Include this in the contract.

• **Again, consult an attorney versed in construction law.**

➤ Should we consider using our contractor's contract?

Sure. If you know, trust, and have confidence in your contractor, by all means consider using his contract. You should, however, still present it to a construction attorney for review.

If you and your attorney want to change the contract in any way, simply cross out, sign, and date what you want to change. Then add an addendum that carries the language you want as part of the contract. Using the contractor's contract does not preclude you from using your preferred bid breakout and strategy. You will want to add copies of the bid, work schedule, and contractor certifications to the contract anyway.

Contractor Warranty

How well do you trust your contractor? Is your contractor a neighbor, a community leader, or seasoned professional? If you follow the selection process in the previous section, you will greatly improve your chances of finding a reputable contractor who will stand behind his work.

It is important to note that you possess maximum leverage on contractors while work is on-going and you still owe the contractor money. After the contractor is fully paid, your leverage is only as strong as your contract, warranty, and finances.

Contractor warranty implies that the contractor is liable to repair and restore any portion of his roadwork that fails within a specified period of time due to construction negligence, misapplication of construction materials, or poor judgment. The warranty period should be specified in the contract.

Blaming your contractor for road failure is not always easy nor is it always correct. Designers, surveyors, or others may be responsible for something built wrong and inadequate. This is where proper job documentation such as written records, video, and photos come in handy. Construction failures that cannot be clearly attributed to the contractor's work may never get solved for many reasons. Consider the following:

1. Be reasonable. The cost to chase a contractor can easily exceed the cost of repairs. Thoroughly evaluate such actions before committing dollars, time, and loss of sleep to something that is just not worth the effort.

2. Keep it in perspective. For reasons including attorney fees, small project magnitude, or landowner oversight, most private roadway projects do not usually tie the contractor to an all-encompassing and detailed legal contract. Conversely, too much contract and not enough project will scare the daylights out of most contractors and may result in contractors demanding less stringent warranty requirements.

3. Fix it now. Deterioration resulting from defective road construction can expand at an alarming rate. You need to protect and preserve your investment. Damages to new road construction must be repaired before costs and scope of work escalate. For this reason alone, it is wise to promptly repair problems, independent of haggling with your original contractor over who is responsible and who pays for repairs. You cannot afford to lose on both fronts.

4. Do you have a case? It's hard to cry for warranty work if, in the first place, you didn't build to some plans or specifications. Likewise, lack of inspection services and not using engineers and consultants will reduce your chances of enticing a contractor to return and do it right.

5. Can you win? Remember, if you are not a repeat customer, some contractors lose interest.

➤ Do any options beyond blind trust exist in holding a contractor to performance standards regardless of project size?

Yes, they do!

Performance bonding. Consider requiring that the contractor post a performance bond insuring that he will perform quality work and perform it on schedule. Schedule requirements include that the contractor begin and end project work according to dates as specified within the contract. Quality is a different issue. Unless you work from engineered plans and employ professional inspectors, it's tough to measure quality and then couple it to a road's longevity. At best, you can contract for materials and quantities that correspond to in-place dimensions (finished work) and hope that it is sufficient to ensure a quality road.

The time period for measuring a road's performance should be a minimum of one year and, preferably, two years. On small projects this obligation may not go over very well and could result in the contractor raising his price accordingly to cover bonding fees. Contractors are also likely to offer higher charges to cover the perceived "hassle factor" in dealing with private individuals or casual neighborhood alliances such as road associations, which may not be able to positively identify lack of quality or performance. In the end, pursuing a performance bond should hinge upon your level of trust for the contractor, magnitude of the project, and additional cost implications relative to including engineered plans, inspections, and bonding fees.

Withhold retainage. Retain this money as a safeguard if the contractor does not perform. How do you know if the contractor is not performing credible work? Hire a third-party construction consultant to observe construction and sign off on the contractor's work. Only pay the retained amount when the consultant has approved or signed off on all work.

Warranty. Require the contractor to sign a legally binding agreement or contract specifying the contractor's obligation to repair and restore any roadway failures up to a certain period of time. Employ the services of a third-party construction consultant to make whatever calls necessary in defining the contractor's obligation, or lack thereof, to repair his work.

Reduce your chances for shoddy work. Strongly consider having a civil engineer draw up construction specifications. On the light side, construction standards can be minimal. Just catching the high points and underlining minimal requirements will give you and your neighbors a standard to hold the contractor against.

Seek an attorney's advice throughout the contract process.

➤ How do we deal with a contractor who doesn't respond when asked to repair faulty work?

Unlike home building or remodeling projects, routine road building products rarely go "bad." Problems you'll most likely encounter originate from one of the four following possibilities:

1. Not enough of the product was used.

2. The product or work is not in the right location.

3. The product was not installed or constructed correctly.

4. The product was never installed or the work never happened in the first place.

So, begin by exhibiting your dated video or photographs of the area in question. Measure what you can. Then review and follow the rules established in your construction agreement. If you can demonstrate that your position is correct and supported within the contract agreement, document your request to the contractor in writing with copies of the photographs. Include alternative language that suggests you might take legal action if the repairs are not completed by a certain date as defined within the warranty period. Hold firm that the contractor complete all repair work commensurate with the terms of the contract.

Concurrently, send duplicate copies of all correspondence including visual evidence to your consultants, attorney, and to all participating neighbors.

Of course, you need to be correct if you level charges against your contractor for alleged incomplete or deficient work. Your contractor may respond by:

- Suing you.

- Turning your account over to a collection agency.

- Placing liens against your and your neighbors' property.

- Reporting you to a credit bureau if your contractor subscribes to that agency.

Depending on the response time or position taken by your contractor, contact your attorney or consulting team for direction.

More Friendly Advice Concerning Contractors

Here's some additional thoughts and advice to consider when evaluating and working with contractors:

• **What you see is usually what you get.** Sloppy personal appearances and beat-up equipment portray a lack of professionalism. This posture can soon become your pain-in-the neck.

• **Trust your judgment.** In spite of references, you may still be unhappy with your contractor. Do as much research as possible and follow your intuition. For instance, contractors that offer extended work guarantees, in-house financing, or that reference you to their "friend in the lending business" should be carefully scrutinized. The same rules of good business apply to road work as they would to any venture involving cash flow and contracts.

• **Contractor referral services.** Contractor referral services are only as good as the screening process they employ. Obviously, you aren't going to be interested in a referral service that values collecting an admission fee and building a contractor list over carefully scrutinizing and evaluating contractors. Use referral services as secondary checks against your own research. If a referral service concurs with your own assessment, you can be confident that the contractor being considered is worthy to pursue.

• **Only pay the general contractor.** Unless you choose to be the general contractor, don't directly pay subcontractors and don't circumvent your general contractor's position and authority on anything. Avoid the hassles of multiple payments, liability, contractor games, and, in the meanwhile, you'll manage to avoid contractor issues that may be based on other projects and issues alien to you and your job. Let the general pay his subcontractors. Pay only the general contractor for work completed.

• **The lowest bid can mean trouble.** Some contractors give intentionally low bids with the idea that there will be opportunity for extra charges as work progresses. Other low bidders may be flat-out incompetent or they haven't put in the time required for a complete estimate. Be wary of bids that are significantly lower than their competitors. Groups of low bids are much better since they act to validate each other. Unless you are accepting a bid for contractual reasons, sign nothing! Choose wisely.

• **Be clear with your contractor.** Do not assume that your contractor knows exactly what you want. Be sure you understand what you want and convey this to the contractor in writing and with pictures. Officially, these pictures and words become your plans and specifications in detailing a desired "look," or standard of construction for your roadway.

• **Favor contractors who ask questions.** Any prospective contractor that you consider should ask you lots of questions. They should be interested and show it by calling you regularly inquiring about the project. Contractors who ask questions demonstrate that they care about your needs and they care about your expectations. A questioning contractor listens and is less likely to sell you something that you do not want or expect to pay for.

Examples of questions that you may field from contractors can include any of the following:

• Who will we report to?

• Who will inspect our work?

• How flexible is your schedule?

• What is the history of this roadway?

• Describe your roadway project to me.

• What do you expect this project to accomplish?

• Do you have the support of all your neighbors?

• Do you have the resources to cover any unexpected costs?

• Tell me what you think is wrong with your road's condition.

• How do you see us working around unsupporting landowners?

• What will be the daily hours of work and will weekend work be allowed?

Take notice of a prospective contractor's body language and patience as you respond to his questions. Do you get a good or flaky feeling while conversing with this person?

• **Assume nothing.** Once under construction, if you ask for the slightest deviation to plan, be prepared to pay for it. If you suspect that a change or deviation in scope of work will result in a net savings for the contractor but it isn't immediately obvious, don't plan on getting an instant credit for the change.

Here's an inside tip: In construction, it seems that changes that benefit you don't get much attention and when they do, they almost always equate to less savings than you had anticipated. However, changes that adversely affect your bottom line seem to manifest themselves at record speed and end up costing you more than you had calculated that they would. Are you guilty of positive thinking, believing that your work credit is worth more than it really is? Perhaps. Still, if your objective is to develop a cost savings or owner credit, prepare yourself and discuss the value of the credit with your contractor before asking him to perform the work.

• **"Intent to Lien" notices.** Once you have signed on with a contractor and he proceeds to order materials, you'll probably receive Intent to Lien Notices from suppliers. Don't be alarmed; this procedure has become commonplace in construction. You're simply being served early notice that you'll be held legally responsible to pay for any construction items that get delivered and used on your project. You'll usually receive these notices before work begins and as your contractor or subcontractor orders additional materials. Pay your bills on time but exchange payment for copies of lien releases for materials used to date. It's crucial that you promptly get written lien releases from those who have sent you notices including the contractor or subcontractor. The headaches inherent in dealing with subcontractor and supplier liens further support the case for hiring a stable and quality general contractor that diligently pays his subcontractors and suppliers.

• **Stay clear of regional problems.** If you feel that your contractor is performing questionable work such as working in a sensitive wetland or waterway without a permit, confront him on the issue. If suspicions persist, contact your local agency to confirm that your construction is in regulatory compliance. If an oil spill or contamination occurs, stay on your contractor to clean it up. Contact your local government and attorney for further direction.

• **Emergency situations.** Depending on who caused what, you may be quite vulnerable during times of emergency repair work. Emergency repairs require fast response and usually result in escalated costs. In some cases, proper construction procedures may be sacrificed along the way. Catastrophic events can put you at the mercy of weather, contractor decision-making, and lots of rented gear. If your contractor is dishonest or at odds with you, anything can happen.

If you get thrust into an emergency situation, there is no need for you to be victimized twice. Even when subject to extreme adverse conditions, there are steps that you can take to protect yourself. Here are a few protective measures:

- Pay for nothing in advance.
- Sign no agreement that leaves open blanks.
- Sign nothing implying longer-term construction than you need.
- Don't be bullied into agreeing to something that you do not want.

- Be suspect of contractors that just happen to have a drove of materials left over from a previous job.

- Decide early on the minimum amount of work that you and your neighbors can afford or live with before committing to more permanent repairs.

- Make all checks out to a company, not an individual, or pay with a credit card. Although nothing is more sincere than cash, these conditions are not appropriate for cash in any denomination!

- If you are in dire need of road repairs and are being forced to post a deposit for action, investigate putting the deposit money into a reputable escrow account to be drawn from as work is completed. This action will also help to protect you in the event you experience any "pass through claims" from subcontractors.

- When you're under the gun, be cautious of cash specials offered by smiling people in old, unmarked, and beat-up trucks.

- With *regional catastrophes*, understand that the likelihood of other neighborhoods needing repairs is also high, so maintain realistic expectations.

- Employ an emergency plan that brings a group of neighbors together quickly, each with a different and concurrent task to perform. Different tasks can include many of the guidelines offered in this book such as taking photographs, checking on the contractor's credentials, organizing a team of neighborhood laborers, and contacting supply houses for materials.

Emergencies require greater scrutiny of contractors and a heightened need for professional advice. Meet with neighbors and craft an emergency action plan that includes the names and phone numbers of all landowners, preresearched consultants, and alternative contractors.

Which Types of Consultants Might We Need?

The number and type of consultants that you may need depends on the conditions of your current road and how you want to improve it. Given a project's complexity and budget, you must determine whether or not consultants are needed. If you decide that you need the services of consultants, here is a list of candidates likely to fit the bill:

➤ The civil engineer.

If you are performing work requiring a construction permit, you will need designed, stamped, and submitted construction plans. A civil engineer performs this type of work. Among the many tasks that civil engineers provide, here are a select few pertinent to roadwork:

- Retaining wall design.
- Permits and entitlement work.
- Erosion control plans and design.
- Asphalt or concrete pavement design.
- Engineering road design including grading and drainage.
- Culvert designs that provide drainage relief and stream flow.
- Construction specifications and details for the contractor to follow.
- Owner representation. Civil engineers work on behalf of private landowners and represent their interests.

Civil engineers can also review and approve contractor pay requests, provide backup paperwork, and confirm contractor quantities as billed. Most civil engineering firms have in-house survey staff and the ability to inspect ongoing work.

➤ The geotechnical engineer.

Serious road problems almost always include soil and soil drainage problems. The geotechnical engineer is qualified to recommend how soil is used, what type of soil is required, and how dense the soil needs to be compacted.

Choosing Engineered Plans and Consultants

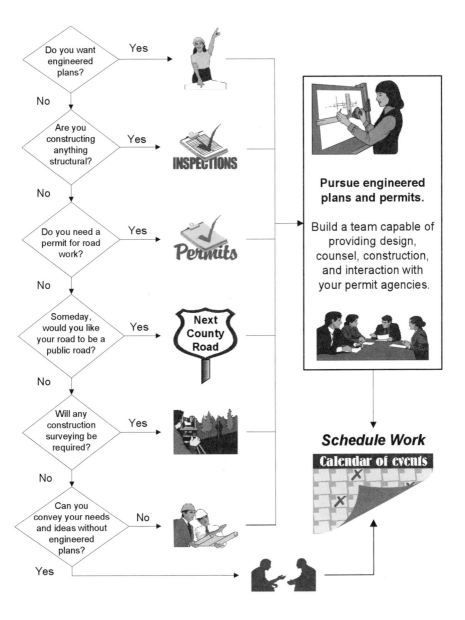

Figure 8-2. Choosing engineered plans and consultants.

If you plan on constructing a hard concrete or asphalt roadway surface, the geotechnical engineer can monitor, test all materials, and ensure construction quality control. Geotechnical engineers rarely perform construction management. If your project requires permitting, a geotechnical evaluation is most likely needed in order to direct the civil engineer how to design portions of the roadway or any retaining wall plans. He is also responsible for documenting all tests, field observations, and contractor activity through a series of daily reports. Geotechnical daily reports may later prove invaluable should post construction problems occur or a dirt-related dispute arise with your contractor. Many private, nonpermitted road projects will construct better and last longer if the services of a geotechnical consultant are employed.

➤ The construction consultant.

The construction consultant knows how to build roads. This consultant can act on your behalf in dealing with other consultants and contractors. The construction consultant helps by monitoring contractor billings and daily construction. If changes to the plan occur, the construction consultant can assist in helping to negotiate new and unknown costs with the contractor. This consultant can help locate credible contractors, review contract documents, confer with attorneys, formulate estimates and the bid format, review the contractor's schedule, and, in general, look out for the landowner's best interests.

Construction consultants can attend road association meetings, take notes, and provide impartial third-party advice. On large projects, competent construction consultants will more than pay for themselves.

➤ An arborist.

If during roadwork a large number of trees need to be pruned or if concerns are raised about tree root damage, an arborist can help make smart decisions to help preserve existing trees. It's important to remember that it is too late to petition an arborist after tree and root damage has occurred. If you plan on using an arborist, consult one *before* construction begins unless you are only interested in after-construction tree planting.

➤ An attorney.

First of all, agree to nothing verbally unless you have supreme trust and confidence in your contractor! Otherwise, get everything in writing.

Second, consult with a construction-oriented attorney. An attorney should be kept on retainer to review contract documents and not just any attorney will do. You need the services of an attorney who deals specifically with land and construction issues. A little real estate experience can't hurt either.

Such an attorney can guide you through the process of drawing up a contract or developing memos of understanding with your contractor. She can advise you as to whether or not a standard architectural AIA construction contract will be adequate, or critique a contractor's contract.

How does the dollar value of your project affect your choice of contract? Does most of your work involve subcontractors or does it make sense to rely on one prime contractor? How do you integrate using a preferred subcontractor with a mix of new subs? The answers depend on many factors, all of which a construction-oriented attorney understands and can act upon.

If you are considering having the contractor sign lien releases in exchange for payments, or perhaps you are seeking specific wording in defining dispute mediation options, an attorney can craft such language into a working contract.

A side benefit of employing a team of consultants offering construction management, geotechnical engineering, and civil engineering services is that they may help minimize your dependence on legal services beyond the need for basic initial and project-ending counsel.

➤ We aren't looking for fully engineered plans. What items absolutely need engineering and design?

Refer to Figure 8-2, the decision tree that describes choosing engineered plans and consultants. What items to include in road design or the degree of engineering detail required depends upon the project. For example, simple projects involving minor road grading and filling potholes may only require a solitary page of specifications describing:

- A minimal bill of materials.

- Erosion control criteria.

- Drainage ditch criteria and after-grading slope treatment.

- Acceptable fabric or grid products and their method of installation.

- Acceptable sources, sizes, and type of rock used in filling potholes.

- Minimal crowning or grading requirements that guarantee drainage.

More complex construction involving road re-alignment, culverts, and structural elements, such as retaining walls and bridges, demand a more intense set of plans and specifications. You'll need the services of at least one professional engineer and a permitted design before commencing with these types of construction.

Some jurisdictions are treating bridges as structures resulting in the need for both a building permit and a road construction (grading) permit. Elaborate road construction elements that usually require multi-discipline, real-world professional engineering include at least the following:

- Rock blasting.

- Retaining walls.

- Adding guardrails.

- Pedestrian tunnels.

- Culverts and subsurface piping.

- Connecting to municipal wet utility lines.
- Precast, cast-in-place, timber, or steel bridge construction.
- Moving overhead utility lines or below-ground dry utilities.
- Roadway surface improvements involving concrete and asphalt.

Seek the advice of your contractor, a civil engineer, and municipal permit agency for the appropriateness and level of engineering required for your specific construction project.

More intense, engineered roadwork increases your need for thorough construction documentation and inspection. Such coverage includes surveying, as-builts, video, and daily monitoring reports. This means hiring qualified consultants to police the contractor and endorse his work. Either the civil engineer or a separate construction consultant can field check the contractor's work for compliance with plans, specifications, and whatever you and your neighbors desire.

Civil engineering may require the additional expertise of a geotechnical consultant to evaluate soils and, in doing so, declare what they will support. Bridge and retaining wall work may require yet another opinion from a third consultant, a structural engineer.

Paying qualified consultants to inspect construction gives you a degree of protection and emphasis that you may need later should any issues or disputes arise. Once you cut the final check and your contractor cashes it, it is difficult to recoup the money. Be sure that you have received everything under contract before paying the last dime.

Finding the Right Consultants

Begin with the yellow pages. Call local real estate development companies and ask their opinion. Who do they use? Why?

Again, look to your local city, county, or state public works department. They should have plenty of possibilities for you to check into. Local material suppliers can recommend both consultants and contractors as can most civil and geotechnical engineers.

Other sources for recommendations include real estate agents and professional societies such as the American Society of Civil Engineers (ASCE).

You Can Volunteer. You Can Help.

Most definitely. In fact, it should be expected from a substantial contingency of your neighbors. It's wise though, to keep in mind what you might get.

It is one thing to write a check to a road association, not be physically present during construction, and then freely drive out for dinner when the paving machine finishes up.

It is another thing to spend a day or so flagging traffic, installing signs, and cleaning out ditches. People respect things that come hard and at a price. Physical labor accomplishes both, especially if the weather isn't cooperating. The glorious result in getting neighbors physically involved is that they will be more proactive in maintaining a road in which they have invested both cash *and* sweat.

Once the road is restored and everyone understands how to maintain his investment, the battle is won. Refer to Figure 6-4. Some examples of volunteer work that can be useful during active construction include:

- Being there when needed.
- Assisting in traffic control.
- Cleaning out culverts, pipes, and ditches.
- Cooking and providing food and refreshments.
- Typing and distributing leaflets to all neighbors.
- Connecting signs to posts and erecting the signs.
- Hand-seeding ditchlines and cut areas after construction.
- Assisting in removing, pruning, and trimming back vegetation.
- Assisting in rolling out, cutting, and laying fabric over the subgrade.

✓ More "Do's"

- Pay for materials delivered to your site.

- Avoid laying out too much money up front.

- Clarify and document communications in writing.

- Make no advance payments for uncompleted work.

- Insist upon and pursue recent contractor references.

- Expect and budget for cost and scope of work overruns.

- Take your time and do things right. Let nobody rush you.

- Learn as much as you can about contracts and contractors.

- When dealing with contractors, pursue, quality, value, and schedule.

- Use an attorney when evaluating or drawing up construction contracts.

- Understand that nothing is more important that using the right contractor.

- Recognize the elements of your project that must be engineered or designed.

- If you don't want your contractor to do something, make it perfectly clear to him.

- Refer to a plan, whether professionally prepared or hand sketched. Don't proceed without a plan.

- Keep people involved and committed by distributing a schedule of volunteer tasks identifying who is responsible for what and when.

CHAPTER 9

Maintaining Your Investment

Ways to Preserve Your Roadway Investment

There exists as many ways to preserve roadways as there are ways to destroy them. *Preservation begins with education.* Education involves getting everyone's cooperation and understanding to adhere to speed and roadway limits. All adjoining landowners must respect the road's edges.

Education leads to more education in that people living on your road should inform delivery companies, service providers, and visitors to respect the road and offer ways to do it. For most people, a subtle reminder is sufficient. People who make a living driving trucks or who own personal vehicles have no desire to damage roads or jeopardize their vehicles. Sure, some oddballs take pleasure in damaging anything: but roads? No, roads are usually damaged out of ignorance, not intent.

➤ Stockpile sand.

If you live in an area prone to snow and ice, stockpile enough sand to get you through the winter. Place these piles strategically where they can be easily accessed and spread over iced areas. Sand should be stockpiled near hills and on steeper or continually damp road surfaces. In addition to being cheap and handy, sand that remains on roads after snowmelt and plowing can work to prevent reicing and enhance traction.

➤ Deicers.

Think twice before deicing with rock salt. Salt will:

- Eat away at asphalt
- Slowly but completely ruin your vehicle.
- Prematurely corrode exposed concrete, steel, and metal piping.
- Possibly impact water supplies, vegetation, and aquatic creatures.

Options to using rock salt include other, milder and non-corrosive salt products, more expensive chemical compounds such as magnesium chloride and calcium chloride, and everyday stock items such as gravel and kitty litter. Organic alternatives include chemicals mixed with various byproducts derived from agricultural processing.

Chemical deicers can be applied to road surfaces before precipitation occurs in order to prevent ice from forming. If the snowfall is heavy enough to dilute chemical deicers, they may become ineffective or result in slush, which can be sanded or plowed. When choosing a deicer, evaluate each product's potential environment impact, method and equipment required for application, cost, the amount you need, and availability. Also inquire at your local highway department and see what they use and why. Then decide what's best for you.

➤ Tools of persuasion.

You may elect to "persuade" uninformed drivers, and, in essence, perform mass education by installing rocks along the road's edges for the purpose of channeling traffic away from ditches, pipe ends, and unimproved shoulders.

Education can also be reinforced with legal-sized roadway signs that tell of speed restrictions, upcoming curves, narrow roadways, turnouts, and sharp grade changes. Don't forget the big dead end sign. Dead end signs say two things: criminals have only one way out and random visitors may be noticed more than they care to be. The result is less traffic.

Other tools of persuasion can include any of the following:

1. Shoulder obstructions that dissuade drivers from entering into ditches, across lawns, or anywhere that you don't want them to travel. See Figure 9-1.

2. Cross-timbers, although unaesthetic, when laid over and across ditches in perpendicular fashion to the road's running surface will prevent vehicles from entering the ditchline.

3. A fence or collection of stout wooden posts placed within the ditchline is highly unpopular with wavering motorists.

4. The type of steel posts (T-Posts) commonly associated with barbed wire work wonders in preventing large trucks from going off road. Truckers greatly respect the protrusions and angle plates sticking out of the sides of these posts (at least those wishing to preserve their tires do). Insert a series of steel fence posts into the ditchline in order to obtain immediate respect.

5. Place larger, ornamental-type rock where vehicles don't belong. Buried below these rocks, install short sections of culvert (length depending on rock size) that are strong enough to support the weight of a rock or other roadway obstruction above. The culverts will be easy to maintain and allow free passage of water. Any rock placed on a ditchline culvert will dissuade people from "ditch driving." Be sure, however, to keep all obstructions clearly out of the travel lanes and wholly on the outer edge of shoulders or within the ditchline.

6. Dig deep ditches. Dig them too deep for anyone to want to drive into.

7. Place a line of rocks between ditchline and the edge of roadway. The rocks should be large enough to discourage drivers from veering into them and high enough to catch the underside of any four-wheel vehicle. Space them close enough to disallow driving or parking between them.

Figure 9-1. Creative use of rock help to discourage wayward vehicles.

➤ These practices (Figure 9-2) will help you to preserve your newly restored road:

• **Check out new vegetation.** Research any vegetative changes along the road's shoulders. Changes include the emergence of any roadside brush, grasses, or trees that haven't been seen before. Questions concerning vegetation changes can be addressed at a local nursery, public extension service, or landscape contractor. Vegetation that thrives in moist conditions unfortunately suggests—that's right—water. Control roadside vegetation in and out of ditches.

• **Watch for changes.** Monitor adjacent land use changes along the roadway. Watch for new driveways and grade modifications. How will these changes affect your roadway?

• **Use four-wheel drive sparingly.** As a group, four-wheel drive vehicles are not engineered for perfect axle-to-axle coordination. That is, when engaged, the front wheels may turn at a different speed than the rear wheels. This ratio varies with vehicle age, vehicle type, manufacturer, and with mechanical wear. Hopefully, the wheels on opposite ends of each axle coordinate with each other but, due to variances in tire condition, mechanical systems, or vehicle structure, they may not. This means that vehicles driven in four-wheel drive may exert forces into your road that work to damage it while also working to slowly tear your vehicle apart. On snow, ice, and mud, slipping wheels and uneven traction conditions largely absorb counter-destructive forces exerted by four-wheel drive vehicles. However, on pavement, where slippage is minimal or nonexistent, real damages to road and vehicle may occur over time due to the actions of four-wheel drive. This condition becomes further exacerbated when fully engaged four-wheel drive vehicles enter curves or make turns. Keep in mind that as distances between spinning wheels on different axles change, the potential for damage increases.

• **Fix new damage.** Look for recent damage to roadway surfaces and repair it immediately. And, never allow anyone to walk a piece of tracked equipment down your hard-surfaced roadway. Track caused damage can be seen in Figures 9-3 and 9-4.

• **Monitor changes in water flow.** During rainfall, watch for water runoff both on and off the roadway. Are the patterns of water flow changing? Is sheet flow turning into a concentrated flow or vice versa? Do you see new scouring or ponding? Investigate these conditions. If these changes indicate destructive action, provide immediate remedies before they turn into larger problems later.

Water volumes that exceed your drainage system may need additional control in the form of detention and storage. You may need to excavate a water holding pond or some sort of storage basin in order to detain and slowly release water heading onto or off of your roadway. Creative ditch solutions may also help in controlling water runoff. Before taking this task on, be sure to seek a civil engineer's opinion or consult with your local public agencies.

Protecting Your Road Investment
Not To Scale

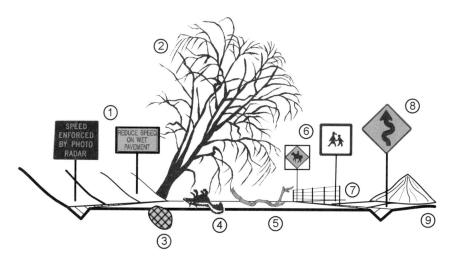

Examples of Ways to Protect Your Road and Ensure Safety

① Post and enforce speed limits and hazard warnings.

② Eliminate dangerous trees and invasive vegetation.

③ Promptly repair road damage and remove emerging rocks as soon as possible.

④ Quickly clean asphalt of road kills.

⑤ Remove sticks and limbs before traffic pushes them into the road's surface.

⑥ Erect signage that warns drivers about children, animals, and other alternative road users.

⑦ Install obstacles that prevent drivers from running into roadside ditches.

⑧ Provide signage that warns drivers about dangerous curves, narrow passages, and unusually steep grades.

⑨ Stockpile sand where ice and snow are expected.

Figure 9-2. Techniques for protecting your road.

Figure 9-3. Results of walking tracked equipment on pavement.

• **Outsmart public service locations.** Place mailboxes and garbage can collection areas in locations that are visible and easy to drive up to and away from. Extend subgrade, drainage relief, and surfacing far enough into these areas to counter truck loading and handle vehicles that may wander too close to the road's edge.

Be sure to allow ample room around these facilities so that vehicles can still safely pass while another is parked at the facility. Roads should be wide enough to accommodate passing vehicles without forcing them to degrade the opposing road edge or drive on the shoulder.

• **Remove road kills.** Remove any and all road kills on your asphalt. Exposed guts pose a health issue and will degrade your paving. Vehicles dodging around road kills also pose a safety hazard.

• **Treat raw dirt and control dust.** Calcium chloride and other chemicals can be added to dirt roadway surfaces in order to help prevent frost heave and to harden base material. A chemical application of calcium chloride will reduce the susceptibility to moisture of finer roadway materials such as silts and clays. It works by first absorbing moisture and completely dissolving. Once dissolved as a liquid, it coats and binds road particles together. The treated soil particles simply become less sensitive to water invasion. Protecting against moisture allows unpaved roadways to hold together longer through severe weather and seasonal changes. This equates to less grading and road maintenance.

Available in both liquid and solid form, calcium chloride also works to reduce dust and erosion potential by the same chemical process. Dry calcium chloride flakes are added to the top 2- to 4-inchs (5 to 10 cm) of roadway and then rolled. As a liquid, calcium chloride is sprayed onto the road's surface. The potential disadvantages of using calcium chloride include its corrosive effect on metals (your vehicle), additional moisture required for setting up in dry climates, and possible contamination of ground water.

Besides calcium chloride, other options for controlling dust include straight water treatment, magnesium chloride, resins, acrylic polymers, and polymer emulsions. Copolymer and organic options are available that meet strict environmental criteria for assuring water quality, however any dust control method you consider should comply with federal EPA standards.

Soil type also helps determine the effectiveness of dust control methods. Course-grained soils may not respond to dust control applications if the soils don't possess enough fines to bind together. Inadequate drainage may also negate effective dust control. Ultimately, you may have to try various treatments before finding an affordable and suitable product for your location, traffic loading, and soil type. Investigate your options when planning for dust control and soil stabilization but remember to check with local authorities before committing to, and investing in, any specific product.

• **Keep in touch.** Keep a list of all core project members and con-tractors handy, including their phone numbers. Distribute this list to your neighbors. Perform after-construction inspections with a neighbor for witnessing purposes and for getting a second opinion.

Is This It? Are We Finished Putting Money into Our Road?

The answer depends on how well the road was built and how the road is used, or abused. As a rule, well-constructed roads are less likely to require additional money and upkeep in the future.

Even well-constructed roads require tune-ups. For instance, there may be a need to grade and add surface rock if snow removal equipment damages the roadway. If a vehicle does not use turnouts and forces an on-coming vehicle into the ditch, some form of ditch restoration may be in order. Land use changes along your road may alter surface drainage enough to mandate additional conveyance and piping.

New driveways and crossroads can cause isolated points of future de-terioration if the impact from added traffic exceeds the road's strength. Formerly sound and dependable roadways can become soft and yield to stress. Quickly restore fresh weak spots to the same level of construction as used during overall road restoration.

New Home Construction and its Impact on Roadways

Land development and home building breeds lots of traffic. If you are experiencing contractors who commute to work along your private road, you may have already witnessed new damages and road deterioration. Dust, nails, and trucks driving on the shoulder are all symptoms of home building activity. Construction vehicles dish out heavier than usual pounding and, in their wake, material deliveries and moving vans follow. It's a natural progression.

And you inherit new, albeit distracted, neighbors who may have er-ratic and uncontrolled driving habits. This alone is reason enough to have predeveloped *road-use rules* on hand when newcomers arrive.

If you live on a road that serves many undeveloped lots, you may be tempted by the thought of stalling road repairs until more lots are occupied. Unless money is the issue (and it usually is), you may grow old waiting to begin work. It is similar to putting off buying a computer until technology slows enough for you to get the most for your buck. It won't, and you may end up incredibly frustrated in the interim.

Learning More

How can you learn more? Begin with your neighbors. Learn together. Solicit input. Draw your neighbors *into* their investment. Appreciate them for being part of the plan. If anyone has another idea or any suggestions on how to make the road project cheaper or better, include his or her opinion.

You can also learn more by tapping the resources available at these locations:

- The library.
- Insurance agencies.
- Schools of civil engineering.
- Public works and municipal offices.
- Construction material supply houses.
- Land and construction-oriented law offices.
- Titleholders such as banks and mortgage brokers.
- Local fire and police departments for access constraints.
- State university extension offices and local agricultural colleges.

Other sources of assistance can be found through local and national contractor associations and professional associations. These organizations have a vested interest in maintaining public relations and many promote public education programs and learning sessions. They are also dependable sources for locating liquid and upstanding contractors.

The most important thing to remember is: know your own limitations. Avoid trial-and-error planning and excessive risk. And, employ specialized experts; they'll save you heartache and money.

Happy Trails

➤ The payback.

A properly constructed road looks and feels good. It is kind to our kids on bicycles, friendly to pedestrians, and easy on our vehicles. This equates to higher resale values when we sell our homes.

Those who are selling their homes off of a decrepit road can easily recoup the cost of grading and rocking the road and even make a handsome profit by rolling the repair costs into the price of their home. People want good, clean access and they are willing to pay for it.

Fixing the road works to ensure a quicker sale and is more likely to encourage higher-income buyers. Higher income people usually drive nice cars and they like to keep them that way. Similar rewards are possible when improving driveways and general access off private roads.

➤ Where does the roadway lead?

Private road standards may someday become commonplace. Specific geometry, grade, and minimum construction requirements may find their way into regulating how and when land is developed. Whether or not such standards could or would preclude people from building on their land remains to be seen. Surely, breakeven points exist for property owners and road associations where their finances expire or the task of physically meeting a minimum road standard remains nearly impossible.

On one hand, safety, conformance, water quality, and dependable and stable access remain of cardinal importance. On the other hand, what can people afford short of receiving public funds? Would public funds ever be available, perhaps in some form of creative financing tailored specifically for private landowners? Would banks and loan institutions freely lend low-cost money for private road projects and, more importantly, would such financing interest private landowners? What about permits? Are public agencies willing to streamline permits, eliminate cost impacts where possible, and reduce fees in order to encourage landowners to improve their roads?

Then, there exists private property rights, easements, and other domain issues. How would you handle old survey mistakes, unexpected geotechnical challenges, increasing easement widths, moving private structures, road re-alignment, storm pond requirements, and...yikes, what a job!

Finally, there's you and me. People living on private roads. Do people want to work together, or, more specifically, how do you nudge them, against their will, to associate and pay for an expensive road project? If the prophet is right and the answer is sprawled on some boxcar or subway wall, head for the tracks, because it will take another book just to explore the possibilities and ramifications involved with universally imposed, private road standards. Meanwhile, go to the last tip.

➤ The last tip.

If this book has baffled you or if you feel technically uncomfortable with its content, you may not be a candidate for doing a road project yourself. If your road association or neighbors feel the same way, you'll be better off hiring a consultant to help wade through the process or to just handle the whole job for you. But, whichever way you go, remember to enjoy the ride!

✓ More "Do's"

- Be ahead of potential repair work; if something can damage your road, it probably will.

- Congratulate yourself; you've just improved your quality of life.

- Enjoy your road!

APPENDICES

Appendix A

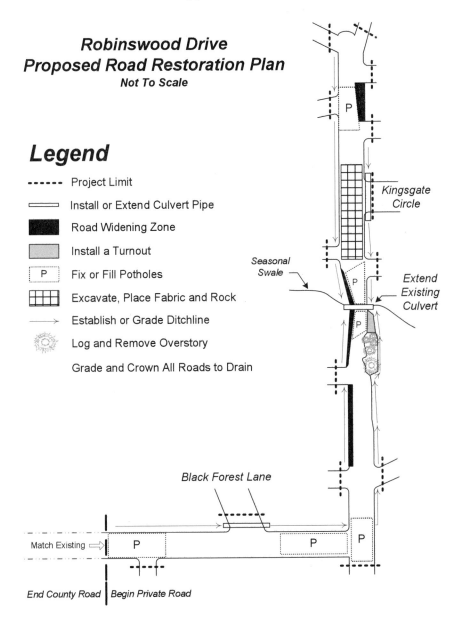

Robinswood Drive
Proposed Road Restoration Plan
Not To Scale

Legend

- - - - - - Project Limit

⟹ Install or Extend Culvert Pipe

█ Road Widening Zone

▓ Install a Turnout

P Fix or Fill Potholes

▦ Excavate, Place Fabric and Rock

→ Establish or Grade Ditchline

❀ Log and Remove Overstory

Grade and Crown All Roads to Drain

Kingsgate Circle

Seasonal Swale

Extend Existing Culvert

Black Forest Lane

Match Existing ⟹

End County Road | Begin Private Road

Figure A-1.

Robinswood Drive Restoration Cost Estimate

Assumptions & Qualifications:

1. All rock to be hauled from Northmen's Rock Quarry.

2. All excess cut material to be hauled and piled at a Robinswood residence.

3. Work on seasonal swale to happen during dry, no-flow conditions.

4. Neighbor work party items 1 through 3 can happen at any time.

5. Contractor profit and risk is included in unit prices.

6. Contractor hourly equipment cost is figured for actual hours of use with no standby costs.

No.	Construction Item and Task	Responsible Party	Quantity	Units	Unit Price	Total Cost
1	Clear Roadside Brush	Landowner Work Party		No Charge		
2	Clean Seasonal Swale Culvert	Landowner Work Party		No Charge		
3	Clean Driveway Culverts	Landowner Work Party		No Charge		
4	Remove Trees at Turnout	Smith's Tree Services	6	Each	$150.00	$900
5	Install 18 inch Culverts	Sitework Contractor	80	Lineal Feet	$19.00	$1,520
6	Lengthen Seasonal Swale Culvert	Sitework Contractor	20	Lineal Feet	$26.50	$530
7	Roadway Fabric	Sitework Contractor	1,100	Sq.Yards	$1.45	$1,595
8	Inorganic Structural Fill	Sitework Contractor	600	Truck C.Y.	$3.25	$1,950
9	6 inch Oversized Crushed Rock	Sitework Contractor	320	Tons	$7.90	$2,528
10	2 inch Base Crushed Rock	Sitework Contractor	950	Tons	$7.35	$6,983
11	5/8 inch Top Course Rock	Sitework Contractor	560	Tons	$7.60	$4,256
12	Road Signs and Posts	Landowners to Purchase	5	Each	$85.00	$425
13	Install Road Signs	Landowner Work Party		No Charge		
14	Trucking - Truck and Trailer	Sitework Contractor	60	Hours	$65.00	$3,900
	Haul Excess to McKey Residence					
	Import Crushed Rock					
15	Move-in and Move-out Charge	Sitework Contractor	1	Lump Sum	$800.00	$800
16	Excavator with Operator	Sitework Contractor	24	Hours	$155.00	$3,720
	Excavate and Install Culverts					
	Excavate and Cut Ditches					
	Excavate Potholes					
	Road Widening and Turnouts					
17	D-5 Sized Dozer with Operator	Sitework Contractor	16	Hours	$140.00	$2,240
	Push Crushed Rock					
	General Purpose Grading					
18	Single Drum Roller (rented)	Sitework Contractor	16	Hours	$125.00	$2,000
19	Road Grader with Operator	Sitework Contractor	20	Hours	$135.00	$2,700
	Fine Grade Subgrade and Ditchline					
	Fine Grade Crushed Rock					
20	Laborers	Sitework Contractor	32	Hours	$26.00	$832
21	Traffic Control & Laborers	Landowners To Provide		No Charge		

Base Restoration Cost:	$36,879
5% Contingency:	$1,844
Subtotal Restoration Budget:	$38,722

Figure A-2.

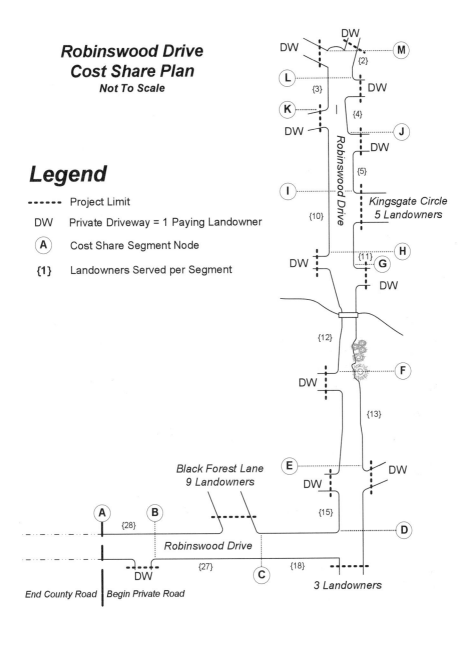

Figure A-3.

Robinswood Drive Cost Share Breakdown
Payment Option 3 - Pay per Lineal Distance of Road Traveled

Base Cost Share Information

1. Total Landowner Tracts: 28
2. Total Restoration Budget: $38,722

3. Total Roadway Restoration Length: 2,190
4. Cost per Lineal Foot: $38,722/ 2,190 feet = Average Cost of $17.68 per lineal foot.

A	B	C	D	E	F	G	H	I
No.	Segment	Segment Length (in feet)	Average Gross Segment Cost	Landowners Served per Segment	Total Shared Cost per Segment	Landowner Cost to Each Segment	Landowners Within each Segment	Gross Contribution per Segment
1	A - B	125	$2,210	28	$79	$79	1	$79
2	B - C	115	$2,033	27	$75	$154	Black Forest Ln. (9)	$1,388
3	C - D	250	$4,420	18	$246	$400	3	$1,199
4	D - E	165	$2,917	15	$194	$594	2	$1,189
5	E - F	265	$4,686	13	$360	$955	1	$955
6	F - G	270	$4,774	12	$398	$1,353	1	$1,353
7	G - H	130	$2,299	11	$209	$1,562	1	$1,562
8	H - I	145	$2,564	10	$256	$1,818	Kingsgate Circle (5)	$9,090
9	I - J	225	$3,978	5	$796	$2,614	1	$2,614
10	J - K	155	$2,741	4	$685	$3,299	1	$3,299
11	K - L	165	$2,917	3	$972	$4,271	1	$4,271
12	L - M	180	$3,183	2	$1,591	$5,862	2	$11,725

Total Length: 2,190

Total Cost: $38,722

Landowner Count Check: 28

Total Cost Check: $38,722

Column A represents segment number.

Column B represents road segments to landowner's driveways and crossroads.

Column C represents the total lineal footage within each road segment.

Column D is the total cost ($38,722) divided by the total length (2,190 feet) and multiplied by column C, lineal footage per segment.

Column E represents the total number of landowners served per segment. For instance, rear segment number 12 serves only two landowners.

Column F is the shared cost per segment derived by dividing the gross segment cost by the total number of landowners served by that segment.

Column G (shaded) defines each landowner's prorated cost. It is derived by cumulating each landowner's individually shared segment costs to their driveway.

* For example, if your land accesses off Segment 4, you pay $594. Off Segment 11, you pay $4,271. Kingsgate Circle landowners each owe $1,818 and so forth.

Columns H and I round-out the analysis.

Ultimately, individual landowner costs range from $79 to $5,862 depending on how far up the road they own land.

Figure A-4.

Robinswood Drive Restoration Cost Estimate
(Metric Version)

Assumptions & Qualifications:

1. All rock to be hauled from Northmen's Rock Quarry.
2. All excess cut material to be hauled and piled at a Robinswood residence.
3. Work on seasonal swale to happen during dry, no-flow conditions.
4. Neighbor work party items 1 through 3 can happen at any time.
5. Contractor profit and risk is included in unit prices.
6. Contractor hourly equipment cost is figured for actual hours of use with no standby costs.

No.	Construction Item and Task	Responsible Party	Quantity	Units	Unit Price	Total Cost
1	Clear Roadside Brush	Landowner Work Party		No Charge		
2	Clean Seasonal Swale Culvert	Landowner Work Party		No Charge		
3	Clean Driveway Culverts	Landowner Work Party		No Charge		
4	Remove Trees at Turnout	Smith's Tree Services	6	Each	$150.00	$900
5	Install 18 inch Culverts	Sitework Contractor	27	Meters	$56.30	$1,520
6	Lengthen Seasonal Swale Culvert	Sitework Contractor	7	Meters	$75.71	$530
7	Roadway Fabric	Sitework Contractor	920	Sq. Meters	$1.73	$1,594
8	Inorganic Structural Fill	Sitework Contractor	460	Cubic Meter	$4.24	$1,950
9	6 inch Oversized Crushed Rock	Sitework Contractor	320	Tons	$7.90	$2,528
10	2 inch Base Crushed Rock	Sitework Contractor	950	Tons	$7.35	$6,983
11	5/8 inch Top Course Rock	Sitework Contractor	560	Tons	$7.60	$4,256
12	Road Signs and Posts	Landowners to Purchase	5	Each	$85.00	$425
13	Install Road Signs	Landowner Work Party		No Charge		
14	Trucking - Truck and Trailer	Sitework Contractor	60	Hours	$65.00	$3,900
	Haul Excess to McKey Residence					
	Import Crushed Rock					
15	Move-in and Move-out Charge	Sitework Contractor	1	Lump Sum	$800.00	$800
16	Excavator with Operator	Sitework Contractor	24	Hours	$155.00	$3,720
	Excavate and Install Culverts					
	Excavate and Cut Ditches					
	Excavate Potholes					
	Road Widening and Turnouts					
17	D-5 Sized Dozer with Operator	Sitework Contractor	16	Hours	$140.00	$2,240
	Push Crushed Rock					
	General Purpose Grading					
18	Single Drum Roller (rented)	Sitework Contractor	16	Hours	$125.00	$2,000
19	Road Grader with Operator	Sitework Contractor	20	Hours	$135.00	$2,700
	Fine Grade Subgrade and Ditchline					
	Fine Grade Crushed Rock					
20	Laborers	Sitework Contractor	32	Hours	$26.00	$832
21	Traffic Control & Laborers	Landowners To Provide		No Charge		

Base Restoration Cost:		$36,878
5% Contingency:		$1,844
Subtotal Restoration Budget:		$38,722

Figure A-5.

Robinswood Drive Cost Share Breakdown
Payment Option 3 - Pay per Lineal Distance of Road Traveled

(Metric Version)

Base Cost Share Information

1. Total Landowner Tracts: 28
2. Total Restoration Budget: $38,722
3. Total Roadway Restoration Length: 730
4. Cost per meter: $38,722/ 730 meters = Average Cost of $53.04 per meter.

A No.	B Segment	C Segment Length (in meters)	D Average Gross Segment Cost	E Landowners Served per Segment	F Total Shared Cost per Segment	G Landowner Cost to Each Segment	H Landowners Within each Segment	I Gross Contribution per Segment
1	A - B	42	$2,228	28	$80	$80	1	$80
2	B - C	38	$2,016	27	$75	$154	Black Forest Ln. (9)	$1,388
3	C - D	83	$4,403	18	$245	$399	3	$1,196
4	D - E	55	$2,917	15	$194	$593	2	$1,187
5	E - F	89	$4,721	13	$363	$956	1	$956
6	F - G	90	$4,774	12	$398	$1,354	1	$1,354
7	G - H	43	$2,281	11	$207	$1,562	1	$1,562
8	H - I	48	$2,546	10	$255	$1,816	Kingsgate Circle (5)	$9,081
9	I - J	75	$3,978	5	$796	$2,612	1	$2,612
10	J - K	52	$2,758	4	$690	$3,301	1	$3,301
11	K - L	55	$2,917	3	$972	$4,274	1	$4,274
12	L - M	60	$3,183	2	$1,591	$5,865	2	$11,731

Total Length: 730

Total Cost: $38,722   Landowner Count Check: 28

Total Cost Check: $38,722

Column A represents segment number.

Column B represents road segments to landowner's driveways and crossroads.

Column C represents the total length within each road segment.

Column D is the total cost ($38,722) divided by the total length (730 meters) and multiplied by column C, length per segment.

Column E represents the total number of landowners served per segment. For instance, rear segment number 12 serves only two landowners.

Column F is the shared cost per segment derived by dividing the gross segment cost by the total number of landowners served by that segment.

Column G (shaded) defines each landowner's prorated cost. It is derived by cumulating each landowner's individually shared segment costs to their driveway.

* For example, if your land accesses off Segment 4, you pay $593. Off Segment 11, you pay $4,274. Kingsgate Circle landowners each owe $1,816 and so forth.

Ultimately, individual landowner costs range from $80 to $5,865 depending on how far up the road they own land.

Columns H and I round-out the analysis.

Figure A-6.

Appendix B

UNIT MEASUREMENT CONVERSION TABLES

English (inch-pound) to metric

1 inch = 25.4 millimeters
1 inch = 2.54 centimeters
1 foot = 3048. millimeters
1 foot = 30.48 centimeters
1 foot = .3048 meters
1 yard = .914 meters
1 mile = 1.6093 kilometers
1 square inch = 6.451 square centimeters
1 square foot = .0929 square meters
1 square yard = .836 square meters
1 square mile = 2.59 square kilometers
1 acre = .405 hectares
1 cubic foot = .028 cubic meters
1 bank cubic yard = .765 cubic meters
1 pound = .453 kilograms

Metric to English (inch-pound)

1 millimeter = .039 inches
1 centimeter = .394 inches
1 centimeter = .033 feet
1 meter = 3.28 feet
1 meter = 1.094 yards
1 kilometer = .621 miles
1 square centimeter = .155 square inch
1 square meter = 10.764 square feet
1 square meter = 1.196 square yards
1 square kilometer = .386 square miles
1 hectare = 2.471 acres
1 cubic meter = 35.3145 cubic feet
1 cubic meter = 1.308 bank cubic yards
1 kilogram = 2.205 pounds

PIPE DIAMETER CONVERSIONS

Selected nominal pipe sizes converted to their metric equivalent.

½ inch nominal converts to 15 mm.
¾ inch nominal converts to 20 mm.
1 inch nominal converts to 25 mm.
2 inch nominal converts to 50 mm.
3 inch nominal converts to 80 mm.
4 inch nominal converts to 100 mm.
6 inch nominal converts to 150 mm.
8 inch nominal converts to 200 mm.
12 inch nominal converts to 300 mm.
18 inch nominal converts to 450 mm.
24 inch nominal converts to 600 mm.
30 inch nominal converts to 750 mm.
36 inch nominal converts to 900 mm.
48 inch nominal converts to 1200 mm.

Appendix C

PROFESSIONAL ASSOCIATIONS
And sources for additional information

American Association
of State Highway and
Transportation Officials
444 North Capitol Street, NW
Suite 249
Washington, D.C. 20001
1-800-231-3475
Website: www.transportation.org

American Concrete Institute
38800 Country Club Drive
Farmington Hills, MI 48331
248-848-3700
Website: www.aci-int.org

American Concrete Pavement
Association
5420 Old Orchard Road, Suite A100
Skokie, Illinois 60077-1059
847-966-2272
Website: www.pavement.com

American Concrete Pipe Association
222 W. Las Colinas Blvd., Suite 641
Irving, Texas 75039
214-506-7216
Website: www.concrete-pipe.org

American Consulting Engineers
Council
1015 15th St., NW, Suite 802
Washington, DC 20005
202-347-7474
Website: www.acec.org

American Institute of Constructors
466 94th Ave. North
St. Petersburg, FL 33702
727-578-0317
Website: www.aicnet.org

American Public Works
Association
2345 Grand Blvd., Suite 500
Kansas City, MO 64108-2625
816-472-2475
Website: www.apwa.net

American Rental Association
1900 19th St.
Moline, IL 61265
309-764-2475
Website: www.ararental.org

American Road & Transportation
Bldrs. Assn.
1010 Massachusetts Ave. NW
Washington, DC 20001
202-289-4434
Website: www.artba.org

American Society of Concrete
Contractors
1801 Royal Lane, Suite 704
Dallas, TX 75229-3168
866-788-2722
Website: www.ascconc.org

The Asphalt Institute
P.O. Box 14052
Lexington, KY 40512-4052
606-288-4960
Website: www.asphaltinstitute.org

Asphalt Recycling and Reclaiming Assn.
3 Church Circle, PMB 250
Annapolis, MD 21401
410-267-0023
Website: www.arra.org

Associated Equipment Distributors
615 W. 22nd St.
Oak Brook, IL 60523
630-574-0650
Website: www.aednet.org

Associated General Contractors of America
333 John Carlyle St.
Alexandria, VA 22314
703-548-3118
Website: www.agc.org

Canadian Association of Equipment Distributors
4531 Southclark Place
Ottawa, ONT K1Y 3V2
613-822-8861
Website: www.caed.org

Concrete Sawing and Drilling Assn.
6089 Frantz Rd., Suite 101
Dublin, OH 43017
614-798-2252
Website: www.csda.org

Equipment Manufacturers Institute
10 S. Riverside Plaza, Suite 1220
Chicago, Il 60606
312-321-1470
Website: www.emi.org

International Concrete Repair Institute
1323 Shepard Dr., Suite-D
Sterling, VA 20164-4428
703-450-0116

International Society of Explosives Engineers
29100 Aurora Road
Cleveland, OH 44139
440-349-4004
Website: www.isee.org

Land Improvement Contractors of America
3060 Ogden Avenue, Suite 304
Lisle, IL 60532
630-548-1984
Website: www.ourworld-top.cs.com/landimprove

National Asphalt Pavement Association
5100 Forbes Blvd.
Lanham, MD 20706-4413
888-468-6499
Website: www.hotmix.org

National Ready Mix Concrete Assn.
900 Spring St.
Silver Spring, MD 20910
301-587-1400
Website: www.nrmca.org

National Society of Professional Engineers
1420 King Street
Alexandria, VA 22314
703-684-2800
Website: www.nspe.org

National Stone, Sand, & Gravel Assn.
2101 Wilson Blvd., Suite 100
Arlington, VA 22201
703-525-8788
Website: www.nssga.org

National Utility Contractors Assn.
4301 N. Fairfax Drive, Suite 360
Arlington, VA 22203-1627
703-358-9300
Website: www.nuca.com

The Road Information Program
1726 M St., NW, #401
Washington, DC 20036
202-466-6706
Website: www.tripnet.org

Underground Contractors Assn.
3158 S. River Rd., Suite 135
Des Plaines, IL 60018-4221
847-299-6930

GLOSSARY

A

as-builts. Construction drawings documenting work as installed or validating work that has been constructed per design and specification.

aspect. The position of land with respect to the four points of the compass.

automobile alignment. A vehicle's wheel alignment.

B

backfill. Process of filling a ditch, depression, or hole in the road with material.

ballast. Heavy and large-sized rock placed to stabilize subgrade and support a road prism.

bank cubic yards. Soil as measured in its original native state, prior to excavation.

base course. The strata of material lying between native material or rock subbase and an upper running course or pavement. Base material is smaller than subbase and larger than top course or running surface rock.

bedrock. Solid rock that is native to the site and underlies topsoil and other nonorganic soil types.

bio-filtration. The process of flowing water over and through living matter in order to filter and purify it.

box culvert. A cheap but effective wooden structure that is built and placed into the surface of a road for purposes of collecting road runoff or for passing water across the road.

bridging. A condition where poor, wet, or unstable soil is successfully crossed or "bridged" over with a combination of engineered fabric or grid and rock, structural soil, or chunk materials.

C

change order. An authorized and written change to the contractor's scope of work, price, or schedule issued after the contract has been executed.

compaction. Consolidating soils or making them dense by rolling, tamping, surcharging, vibrating, or soaking.

contamination. Refers to a condition where a lesser quality road material permeates and mixes with a higher quality road material. An example of contamination would be mixing native, organic soils with clean imported structural fill material.

corduroy. Logs placed into the subgrade of a road, perpendicular to centerline, for purposes of supporting traffic.

cost contingency. A budgeted amount of funds held to pay for unexpected cost overruns. Contingencies are usually determined by taking a percentage of the total expected project cost and adding it to the construction cost grand total. The percentage in roadwork usually ranges from 5 to 15 percent depending on the project's complexity, weather, and duration.

crowned. Grading a road's surface so the centerline of the road is higher than either roadway edge or shoulder. Crowning is meant to shed water evenly to both sides of a roadway. Proper crowning results in a roadway profile that rises evenly from one edge of the roadway towards the roadway center and then down to the opposite roadway edge.

crushed base material. Crushed base rock.

crushed rock. The final product derived from crushing larger, naturally shaped rock or large rock fragments into a smaller sized product.

crushing. Process of reducing larger rock into a smaller, uniform, fractured state that is conducive to engineering, design, and stable construction. Crushing produces a better rock product since it finds and eliminates naturally occurring microscopic seams and fractures common to bulk, larger rock.

culvert. In terms of road building, culverts are buried structures that allow water to pass under roadways and embankments. A culvert is an enclosed pipe or concrete box structure but it is not a bridge, although both bridges and culverts can work to accomplish the same objective of allowing free-flowing water to pass under a roadway. Culverts are usually round or arched.

cut. Removing or grading earth. An excavation where part of the road is removed in order to generate fill material or alter the road's grade.

D

debris. Deleterious material or trash responsible for clogging ditches and culverts. Natural debris can be comprised of twigs, leaves, live vegetation, sand, or soil.

differential settling. Uneven movement or lowering of random sections of a roadway or ground.

dirt. Slang for native earth. Material that is generally unsuitable for construction purposes. Topsoil or contaminated material is commonly referred to as dirt. If excavated native material is suitable for construction use, it may be called any number of redeeming names

such as select, till, structural, etc.

ditch. A trough or narrow trench that runs parallel to and alongside a roadway for purposes of collecting and channeling water runoff away from the roadway.

ditchline. The alignment or centerline location of a ditch.

do-it-yourselfer. Someone who is not a road construction professional yet is willing to perform a road restoration project through his own efforts, on his own time.

drainage. The movement of water across or through soil.

draw. A payment to the contractor for completed and accepted work. A draw schedule is a time-driven pay cycle.

driveway. Lateral access off of a road to one's property, home, or place of business.

dry utilities. Utilities that do not contain water including power, phone, gas, cable television, data transmission, and communication lines.

E

embankment. A fill that supports a roadway. Embankments exhibit a slope that drops down and away from the roadway shoulder, ditch, or roadway's outer edge.

erosion control. The act of stopping and controlling soil erosion as caused by the abrasive actions of wind, water, or mechanical movement.

excavation. The act of cutting earth to manipulate a roadway location or grade.

F

fabric. An engineered woven product widely used around the world to enhance road building and restoration. See geotextile.

fill. Calculated accumulation of material required to fill a hole, raise road grades, or establish a road location higher than that allowed by its natural location or topography.

fill material. Concerning road building, fill material is quality material or crushed rock aggregate suitable to be used as a roadway building constituent.

fractured. Cracked, split, or separated rock, asphalt, or concrete.

free-draining material. Granular fill that will allow water to freely migrate and pass through without building up or clogging. Material of this nature is silt-free and organic-free and usually has sand or rock as one of its components.

French drain. A below-ground water collection system of varying length that intercepts subsurface flow and conveys it to a point of discharge. French drain systems are an effective tool used in catching migrating ground water before it reaches a road's subgrade. Points of discharge usually include existing creek channels, storm systems, or onto adjoining land that is *below* and away from the road's subgrade. French drains are constructed in trenches by surrounding perforated plastic pipe within gravel or rock backfill. Depending on soil conditions, a blanket of free-draining fabric may be placed as a separator between the French drain and native trench excavation.

frontage. A road that borders or fronts property.

G

geogrids. An engineered, non-woven, one-piece polymer product formed into lightweight, grid-like sheets with geometric openings resembling a network or mosaic of tendons. Geogrids come in rolls and are laid over soil and rock material in order to provide physical reinforcement, hold aggregate, or separate material. Grid is used widely around the world to enhance soil strength in construction applications and can be found at local distribution and contractor supply outlets.

geotextiles. Woven or non-woven, flexible fabrics comprised of synthetic polymers. These products come in rolls of varying width and provide many functions including separating soil from water, reinforcing soil or fill material, providing drainage within soils, or, when impregnated, forming an impenetrable barrier. Geotextiles are cheap, lightweight, and easy to install. Commercial geotextiles come in many grades and weights. These products can be found at local distribution and contractor supply outlets.

graded or grading. Treating a road surface by use of a road grader, bulldozer, or other heavy equipment with a blade. Grading results in a more uniform and level surface with little distortion and irregularities. Grading can also imply pushing loose material along a roadway, mass excavation, or removing accumulations such as snow.

granular soil. Sandy, rocky, and coarse soil possessing minimal silts and clays.

gravel. Processed gravel is uniform and small rock up to 2½-inches in diameter. It can be round or crushed. Naturally occurring gravel is a mixture of sand, cobbles, and boulders, with minimal fines.

groundwater. Water that exists in either a static or moving state below the ground's surface.

grid. Short for geogrid.

ground water. Water existing below the ground's surface under a road.

H

headroom. The distance measured vertically between the outside top of a culvert pipe and the road surface above.

I

improved roadway. Any roadway that is paved or well-surfaced, and maintained.

infiltration. The movement of water horizontally or vertically through soil, asphalt, concrete, or fractured rock.

inslope. The act of grading a road's surface so as to allow it to drain *in* towards the cut slope or in the direction of the roadway's uphill side.

L

lift. A layer of material, rock or paving added to a road.

M

maintenance. Caring for a roadway. Grading, repairing, maintaining signs, and cleaning ditches are all indications of maintenance.

material. Commonly referred to as any suitable fill other than rock used to build and restore roadways.

materials-on-hand. These are materials procured by the contractor but not yet installed. They may have been purchased together with other materials to capitalize on quantity cost savings or with the goal of saving on trucking and delivery costs. Since most contracts stipulate paying contractors only for work completed, materials-on-hand can be a burdensome cost for any contractor to carry.

mineral soil. Nonorganic native soil.

minus crushed rock. A crushed rock product where the largest rock size piece does not exceed the stated size in any dimension. Crushed rock with any "minus" designation is generally purchased from a pit and is manufactured by crushing larger rock into whatever size smaller rock is desired. A minus designation indicates that smaller rock pieces and fine rock particles are also included as part of the final crushed rock product.

N

nonvibratory compactor. A compactor that compresses the soil through sheer weight and repetition without relying on vibration or shaking.

O

organics. Dead or living organic matter and vegetation. Organics are a constituent of topsoil. Soil containing organics is not suitable for roadway construction.

overexcavation. As used in this book, describes the unintended event of excavating below grade in order to remove unsuitable or wet dirt, rock, or organic and woody material, and then replacing it with imported suitable and structural material.

overlay. Placing new pavement directly over and onto the surface of existing pavement.

outslope. The act of grading a roadway to drain *out* towards the downhill side or away from the uphill side of a roadway.

P

pass-through-claims. Subcontractor claims for damages that come your way on behalf of the general contractor that is under contract with you.

perforated pipe. Pipe with slots or holes cut through the pipe so as to allow the free passage of water either out of or into the pipe.

pipe bedding. Free-draining rock, sand, or gravel that is used as support and fill around pipes and culverts.

pit-run. A natural material comprised of cobbles, gravel, sand, and fines. Suitable and native fill material derived straight from a pit without any processing. Also known as *bank gravel*.

pothole. A roadway failure resulting in a depression or hole.

potholing. The practice of excavating holes within a roadway to measure the depth of existing utilities, investigate subsurface soil and water conditions, or determine the depth of roadway materials such as rock and asphalt.

private landowners. People who own and control land that may rely on privately owned and maintained roadway access. (See *road association*.)

prism. The cross-sectional geometric shape of a road including subgrade and surfacing.

punchlist. A list of contract deficiencies or unacceptable project work. Final payment and retainage releases can be tied to the contractor's successful completion of all punchlist items.

R

restoration. The act of repairing or restoring a roadway to its former condition or to an improved state.

retainage. An amount or percentage of money earned but withheld from a contractor by the owner for reasons of guaranteeing performance, quality, and completeness of contract work.

retaining structures. A wall. Any system or structure built for purposes of supporting an earthen slope or roadway embankment.

road association. An organized group of private citizens; usually neighbors who have an interest in maintaining commonly owned land and property. (See *private landowners*.)

road compaction. The process of compressing soil into a smaller volume or greater density resulting in fewer air voids between soil particles and greater soil stability.

road grade. A road's vertical pitch, incline, or finished surface.

road memory. A condition that develops over time to where a road forms a "memory" of rolling patterns or a series of failures as related to repetitive traffic flow, loading, and vehicle speed.

road prism. The cross-section and geometric shape of a finished roadway complete with ditchlines, cuts, and fills. Combined levels of cut, fill, subgrade, subbase, base, and running course all define a road's prism.

road ripping. The act of inserting a digging device into a road surface and ripping it. Ripping is usually accomplished with a road grader, excavator, or bulldozer equipped with a ripper attachment or teeth.

road shoulder. The area between a road's running surface and its ditchline, or a fill-slope embankment, or the bottom of a cut slope.

road standard. A minimum level of design, construction, and quality as stipulated by an owner, a municipality, or a road designer.

roadway alignment. The longitudinal or centerline positioning of a roadway as it was built to negotiate topography, water, and land ownership, or to comply with construction design standards.

running course. The final, top course of a roadway including gravel, asphalt, and concrete surfaces.

runoff. Surface water movement resulting from precipitation.

S

sawcut. A method to cleanly cut and remove hard pavement under repair.

scope of work. The objective and extent of work to be accomplished by the contractor.

scouring. The removal of earth due to the force of running water. Erosion.

segregation. The separation of rock from an asphalt mix resulting from movement and vibration.

select material. Free draining and suitable fill material.

sight distance. The limit of distance that one can safely see while operating a vehicle. Sight distance is affected by vehicle speed, roadway curves and grades, locations of driveways, and surrounding obstacles such as retaining walls and vegetation.

silty soil. Soil containing particles finer than sand and coarser than clay.

slope failure. The movement or separation of a road's subgrade, cut, or fill slope.

slope. Road slope refers to the grade or pitch of a road's surface. It also refers to the steepness of a road cut or fill embankment. Slope is determined by measuring vertical gain against horizontal run.

smooth or river rock. Rock in its natural rounded shape and condition.

soft spots. Rotten areas within a road that flex and are subject to deformation under traffic loading. Soft spots result from water infiltration, poor construction, and poor soils.

soil bearing capacity. The amount of loading a soil can support without failure.

specifications. Minimum measurable parameters to which a project is to be constructed. Specifications are project specific and derive from an overall menu of standards.

standards. An all-encompassing set of minimal requirements for construction within a jurisdiction and acceptable to whomever is controlling the project. Standards are the root of specifications.

static compactor or roller. A nonvibratory compactor.

stratum. A layer or zone of road building material, topsoil, or bedrock.

street available fill. Unclassified fill that does not come from a sanctioned source or certified pit. Street available fill usually comes from another construction site where quality native material is being excavated and removed.

subbase. That strata of material between the underlying native subgrade and upper base course. Subbase material is larger than base course.

subcontractor. A specialty contractor under contract to a general contractor who is, in turn, under contract to a project owner. Subcontractors are usually not directly under contract to an owner.

subgrade. Native prepared mineral soil ready for fill, rock, or surfacing.

suitable fill. Inorganic and compactable structural fill.

surface water. Water exposed and sitting on the surface of the ground or roadway.

survey control. The means by which construction is measured, marked, and by which roads are located.

T

through cut. An excavation through earth resulting in walls or slopes rising up from either side of the cut.

trenching. Long and narrow excavation.

trucking or hauling. Method by which construction rock and materials are delivered or hauled away.

turnout. An area integral to, or adjacent to, the shoulder of a road and large enough to admit one or more vehicles.

U

unimproved roadway. An unmaintained and rough roadway that promises surprises for all who dare to venture upon it.

utilities. Systems of pipe, conduit, and wire that can include any one of the following services: storm, sewer, water, power, gas, telephone, cable television, data, and communication lines.

W

weekend warrior. Someone who may or may not be a road construction professional yet is willing to perform a road restoration project over a period of time, usually on weekends.

whiteheads. Concrete pothole plugs that slowly rise above the road's surface.

white-topping. A concrete overlay.

wet utilities. Water borne services namely: sanitary sewer, storm sewer, and water transmission lines.

INDEX

How to Order:

BY FAX: Complete the order form and fax it with credit card information to: **(425) 222-6864**

BY MAIL: Send order form and payment to: **Trans Mountain Publishing P.O. Box 1089 Fall City, WA 98024**

ONLINE: Order online at **transmtn.com.**

EMAIL: RodJohnston@transmtn.com

Shipping and Handling Charge ➤

Domestic Ground: $4.50 for the first book or disk and $2.00 for each additional product.

Domestic Second Day Air: $14.00 for the first book or disk and $4.00 for each additional product.

Domestic Next Day Air: $24.00 for the first book or disk and $4.00 for each additional product.

Canadian Post: $10.00 for the first book or disk and $3.00 for each additional product.

Canadian Courier: $30.00 for the first book or disk and $6.00 for each additional product.

International Air Mail: $18.00 for the first book or disk and $7.00 for each additional product.

ORDER FORM

PLEASE SEND ME THE FOLLOWING:

Send_____ Copy(ies) of ***The Road Repair Handbook*** @ $19.95 each.	$
Send_____ Copy(ies) of ***The Road Repair Handbook*/Robinswood Drive Spreadsheet Files** on CD-Rom or 3½″ Floppy disk @ $20.00 each. (Copies of the four Excel 2000 for Windows, Robinswood Drive Spreadsheet Files, Exhibits A-2, A-4, A-5, and A-6 are available on disk.) Please indicate your choice: ☐ CD-Rom or ☐ 3½″ Floppy	$
Merchandise Total	$
Tax (Washington State addresses, add 8.4%)	$
Shipping and Handling Charge	$
TOTAL	$

SHIP TO:

Name: _____

Company: _____

Address: _____

City: _____ State: _____ Zip: _____

Country: _____ E-mail: _____

Telephone: _____

PAYMENT:

☐ Check payable to **Trans Mountain Publishing**

☐ Charge to: ☐ VISA   ☐ MasterCard   ☐ American Express   ☐ Discover

Name on Card: _____

Signature: _____

Card number: _____ Expires: _____

All prices are in U.S. funds. Please allow 4 to 6 weeks for delivery. Corporations, government agencies, associations, schools, and catalogers, for discount information, please E-mail, fax, or write us.